HOW HUMAN IS HUMAN?

JAPAN LIBRARY

HOW HUMAN IS HUMAN?

THE VIEW FROM ROBOTICS RESEARCH

ISHIGURO Hiroshi

TRANSLATED BY Tony Gonzalez

Japan Publishing Industry Foundation for Culture

Note: Japanese names appearing in this book are given in Japanese order, with the family name first.

How Human Is Human?: The View from Robotics Research
Ishiguro Hiroshi. Translated by Tony Gonzalez.

Published by
Japan Publishing Industry Foundation for Culture (JPIC)
2-2-30 Kanda-Jinbocho, Chiyoda-ku, Tokyo 101-0051, Japan

First English edition: March 2020

This book is a translation of *Dōsureba hito o tsukureruka: Andoroido ni natta watashi* (Shinchosha Publishing Co., Ltd.). The hardcover edition was published in April 2011, and the paperback edition, with the addition of chapters 10 and 12, in 2014.

English publishing rights arranged with the author.
Translation of "Über den Bergen" on p. 106 © Jakob Kellner. Used with permission.

Jacket and cover design: Miki Kazuhiko, Ampersand Works

Printed in Japan
ISBN 978-4-86658-137-8
https://japanlibrary.jpic.or.jp/

Prologue

Imagine an android that looks exactly like you. I suspect just about everyone has thought of something like that at least once in their life. I certainly have. I've even built one. So what did I learn by creating an android that looked exactly like myself? What did it feel like? In a word, it was a far richer experience than I expected. I found that my android was not simply a recreation of my physical self, but a channel through which to consider the very essence of humanity. My android was a mirror held up to my soul, reflecting my inner self rather than my outer self. This book recounts and reflects on that experience and other encounters with androids.

I am a robotics researcher. In Japanese we use a more rigid term to describe my field, "robot engineering," but to my ears that implies a focus on simply building robots. My research aims at something broader: discovering how robots can help us to better understand humanity. For that reason, I prefer the term "robotics researcher." Androids in particular have much to teach us about being human.

Some of the experiences described in this book have already been addressed through research. Others, however, need to be more deeply investigated in the future. I wrote this book bit by bit as I performed my research, so that it became a record of my how my thinking evolved and the key issues I wanted to investigate. The chapters that follow do not simply relate previous research results; in many places they also describe in real time what I was thinking as I carried out particular experiments, along with notes about topics I will need to address in the future. When conducting android research, questions constantly arise and fade away in my mind. The book's contents reflect that cycle. This is not a straightforward story with a clear conclusion. Some of what I have written may even sound absurd. For this, I beg your forbearance.

I believe this book will show my android research to be unlike anything done in the past—unlike what *could* have been done in the past, even. I have discovered a world like no other, one that remains unknown even to most engineers. Some people consider me to be something of a "mad scientist," yet when I present my research at academic conferences, I receive relatively few questions about the engineering aspects of my work. Rather, my audiences tend to ask abstract questions about its human aspects, such as what I learned through creating my androids. I suspect this is because people are more interested in the broader possibilities that androids present than in the equations behind carefully constructed experiments. By describing my own experiences researching androids, I hope to provide some guidance to other researchers in this field.

I also hope to show that the possibilities inherent in androids are not limited to robotics. Androids are closely linked to other fields including cognitive science, neuroscience, and philosophy, and this can prompt deeper questions about the nature of humanity and our own identities. Even if you are not an academic, I hope this book will spark an interest in the potential of androids and provide an opportunity for us to consider our nature together.

CONTENTS

Prologue ... 3

CHAPTER 1 **FROM DAILY-LIFE ROBOTS TO ANDROIDS** ... 7

Research on "daily-life" robots 8 / A semiautonomous greeter robot 10 / Areas of ambiguity 12 / The human form is the ultimate form 14 / Women and children first 15

CHAPTER 2 **REMOTELY CONTROLLED ANDROIDS** ... 19

Creating a new self 20 / Creating another female android 22 / Choosing models 24

CHAPTER 3 **A WORLD OF SURROGATES** ... 29

The post-Geminoid world 30 / Life with surrogates 31 / Androids are becoming a reality in the US 31 / "You look a lot like your synth" 34 / The real you 35

CHAPTER 4 **BECOMING AN ANDROID** ... 39

Questioning MRI 40 / Awareness of the "I" within 42 / The self we see, the self others see 45 / Creating expressions 48 / The embarrassment of our inner workings 51 / Which is the most attractive: face, clothing, or hair? 53 / The finishing touch: clothing 55 / The other me 61

CHAPTER 5 **ADAPTING TO GEMINOIDS** ... 63

Like your own body 64 / Attractive people and performers make the best operators 67 / Second- and third-person viewpoints 70 / The Geminoid homunculus 72 / Operated operators 76 / Operating androids to recall memories 77

CHAPTER 6 **RELATIONSHIPS WITH GEMINOIDS** ... 79

Our experiment in Austria 80 / Emotions communicate better than words 82 / Touching Geminoid F 86 / Lowered mental barriers 89 / What about love? 92

CHAPTER 7   ANOTHER YOU ... 95

Geminoid as a sounding board 96 / A convincing conversation partner 97 / More human than humans? 99

CHAPTER 8   ANDROIDS EXCEEDING HUMANS ... 101

The origins of android theater 102 / An elusive ephemerality 103 / "No human is that pretty" 108 / Beauty is not humanlike 109 / Do people really want to be beautiful? 109 / You, standing right before your own eyes 110 / When a stranger controls you better than you do 111 / An independent being on stage 112

CHAPTER 9   MAKING OURSELVES LIKE ANDROIDS ... 115

Changing androids, changing humans 116 / Thinner than Geminoid 119 / What to fix 120 / Moles and identity 122 / The remarkable similarity between cosmetic surgery and android fabrication 124 / Unnoticed changes in appearances 125 / The link between physical and mental youth 126 / Age and identity 128

CHAPTER 10   PORTABLE GEMINOIDS ... 131

The birth of Geminoid HI-4 132 / A simpler Geminoid with a focus on conversational abilities 133 / A portable Geminoid as a self-substitute 134 / Giving lectures via Geminoid HI-4 136 / My Geminoid receives an invitation 137 / Sharing experiences with Geminoid 139 / Androids as comedians 140

CHAPTER 11   MINIMAL HUMAN DESIGN: TELENOIDS ... 143

Creating a minimal human 144 / Humanness without extraneous elements 145 / "I can't stop touching it" 147 / Children, couples, and the elderly 150 / Robots as a substitute for mobile phones 153 / A new kind of cell phone 155 / True beauty comes from the imagination 157 / Gestures, voices, and smells 158

CHAPTER 12   A MINIMAL MEDIUM FOR SENSING PRESENCE: HUGVIE ... 161

The principle of minimal design 162 / Hugvies relieve stress 164 / Children and Hugvie 165 / How the brain recognizes humans 165

Epilogue ... 169

Acknowledgements ... 174

About the Author ... 175

About the Translator ... 175

CHAPTER
1

FROM DAILY-LIFE ROBOTS TO ANDROIDS

Research on "daily-life" robots

My interest in androids—in other words, humanlike robots—did not arise from thin air. Rather, it developed out of significant questions that occurred to me over long years of robotics research. In this chapter, I describe why I started researching androids and how I began to investigate myself through them. I describe in simple terms my interests and research themes, as well as some of the robots I developed.

I first became seriously engaged in robotics research as a Ph.D. student at Osaka University's Graduate School of Engineering Science. At the time, I was looking for ways to allow robots to function autonomously through environmental recognition based on visual information obtained from cameras. Following that, I served as a research assistant at the University of Yamanashi and at Osaka University, then as an associate professor at Kyoto University. There, my supervisor Ishida Toru told me, "If you're going to be a researcher, you might as well pursue research that will change the world. How about building a robot that can move around the campus here?" Those words became a turning point in my career. Previously, my focus was on fundamental robotics research for industrial applications, so all I really cared about was whether my robots could function in a laboratory. Actually, I was so deeply engaged in image processing research that I considered robots to be little more than vehicles for carrying cameras. However, Professor Ishida's words made me stop and think. What should my research be about? What did I hope to invent? What were my goals? If I was going to create robots, shouldn't I try to develop something entirely new? That's when I decided to build a robot that could perform everyday tasks and interact with people.

Previous robotics research had been primarily concerned with designing robots to work in factories. Japan had already achieved great success in that field, producing some seventy percent of industrial robots worldwide. If I was going to change the world, I needed to build not factory robots but those capable of interacting with humans in daily-life scenarios. My first step toward that goal would be a robot that could roam our campus.

However, I had little interest in creating a robot capable only of simple physical tasks like carrying things around; that would hardly be different from the research already performed by so many others in a factory context. But what, exactly, separated "daily-life" robots from their well-studied factory counterparts? Without clarifying that fundamental difference, my research would never produce a robot that could truly work in everyday situations.

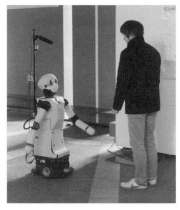

The "daily-life" robot Robovie, developed at ATR Intelligent Robotics and Communication Laboratories.

After some thought, I concluded that the primary difference lay in whether or not the robot interacted with humans. Within factories, robot and human work zones are strictly divided. However, no such clear boundaries exist in everyday scenarios. If I didn't develop a robot that could interact with humans on humanlike terms, I would never create one capable of providing people with services in their normal environment.

Over fifteen years have passed since I embarked on this study of work in everyday situations. Pursuing this research took me from Kyoto University to the ATR Intelligent Robotics and Communication (IRC) Laboratories, where I now develop most of my research projects. Today I pursue my robotics research while serving as a professor at Osaka University and a visiting researcher at IRC.

The first robot I created at IRC was called "Robovie." Following research and development in our laboratory, Robovie is now used for demonstrations in elementary schools, science museums, and shopping malls. When a robot you've developed moves from the laboratory to an actual use scenario, the difficulties inherent in robots that interact with people become clear. It is of course vital when developing fundamental robotic functions to study interactions with humans under controlled laboratory conditions. However, laboratories do not reflect the real world. We must therefore also learn how people regard robots, what kind of relationships arise between humans and robots, and even whether any kind of relationship is possible. To discover and solve such basic problems, it is extremely important to test our creations in real-life scenarios. That's what is happening every time Robovie greets a visitor at a shopping mall.

A semiautonomous greeter robot

Developing a robot designed to interact with humans during their daily activities requires a far broader range of technical innovation than developing one for factory applications. The latter only requires research in two areas: how to create the robot's physical mechanisms and how to program the software it needs to perform its tasks. In contrast, a robot designed for daily use additionally requires a sensor network capable of recognizing human and robotic activities.

Of course, a robot capable of humanlike vision and cognition could use its own senses to recognize human behavior, but our current technology does not allow for that. Instantaneously providing the robot with the information it requires to operate therefore involves installing sensors throughout its surroundings. For example, installing many cameras in the environment allows for rapid detection of people's locations and activities, along with observation of how the robot and humans are interacting.

It is also far more difficult to develop the mechanisms and software for these robots than for industrial robots. Hardware and software for robots working in factories need only be designed to efficiently perform a given task, making development relatively straightforward. However, if the robot is to function well in real-life situations, it potentially needs to perform many more tasks—tasks that are currently difficult for researchers to predict. In order to create robots that support human activities, we must therefore advance our understanding of how people behave.

Sensor networks can play a role in grasping human behavior. Several years ago I developed a sensor network and experimental system including a robot capable of providing services, if only in a semiautonomous fashion. Since then, I have tested this system in a variety of situations. By "semiautonomous," I mean a robot that does not make all decisions for itself—human beings must sometimes intervene via the Internet to aid the robot's cognitive behavior. In this case, the robot was designed to give people directions.

The robot uses a sensor network that includes a laser rangefinder and multiple cameras to detect the locations of people in its environment. Variations in lighting can cause cameras to lose track of human figures, but laser rangefinders do not suffer from this limitation. This sensor network can thus reliably track the motions of humans and robots. Further, its cameras recognize facial expressions, allowing it to make predictions of the emotional state of people in the environment.

The robot can engage in semiautonomous activities based on information from this sensor network. Its objective is to use sensor network functions to accurately detect people in the environment who appear to be lost, approach them, and offer directions. The system can also make predictions about the directions in which people are moving, allowing the robot to move to a location at which it can intercept its target. Functions up to this point are all autonomously performed.

It is difficult, however, to fully automate conversations with people. In locations like a shopping mall, background noise is very loud. The robot is equipped with a microphone and a simple speech recognition system, but noise makes speech recognition impossible when the speaker is located even one meter from the microphone. To address this issue, a human operator listens to conversations with the robot over the Internet and decides what the robot should do next.

Once the robot's next action is determined, it returns to autonomous behavior. For example, if instructed to guide the user to a store entrance, it can use sensor network information to perform this task on its own.

Of course, this raises an obvious question: If each robot requires a human operator, what's the point of using robots in the first place? But recall that human intervention is only required when the robot is conversing with someone; most of the time, it behaves autonomously. Roughly speaking, a human operator is needed only around ten percent of the time that the robot is active. Creative handling can allow a human operator to manage ten robots at once. This means one person can do the work of ten, making this a highly practical system.

Remote operations provide various other benefits as well, such as allowing safe operation in hazardous locations. For instance, if night patrols in a dangerous neighborhood are required, using a remotely controlled robot to perform this task would be much safer than deploying human patrols. Further, such a robot can be operated from anywhere in the world with Internet access, be it a workplace, a home, or, in the case of an emergency, even a hotel while on vacation. When the time for a shift change comes, duties can be handed off to anyone else with Internet access.

Clearly, the potential exists for a revolution in the way that we interact with our world through robots.

Areas of ambiguity

Advancing my research into daily-life robots and performing experiments to confirm their potential made me once again question just what a robot is.

I had created a prototype for a guidance robot, but I remained unsure of how confident I could be in its design. As mentioned above, the full system included several components. What bothered me was whether I had optimally designed those components to accommodate all situations, or whether a more "perfect" design was possible. Upon reflection, I realized I was dissatisfied with nearly all parts of the system.

When designing robotic mechanisms, we can reference conventional technologies to determine methods for optimally controlling those mechanisms, specifically for performing the most appropriate operations.

But how can we be sure that some better solution for the mechanism design does not exist? For example, my guidance robot moved on wheels. Should such a robot have two wheels, or three? Or should it be bipedal? In actual designs for most robots, these decisions are not made with complete certainty. Rather, many aspects of the design are based on the engineer's intuition. Of course, it is impossible to place hard numbers on what ratio of the system is optimally designed and what parts are not, but for argument's sake, let's say that around seventy to eighty percent of the system design is based on intuition, without any firm basis for why it turned out the way it did.

Not that there's necessarily anything wrong with that. I would just like to point out that such areas of ambiguity present interesting opportunities for future research. Indeed, the search for detailed reasoning behind a given design will likely produce new technologies and areas for exploration. In that sense, robotics is a gold mine of research themes, with many rich veins still left to explore.

Among these areas of ambiguity, I felt the appearance of my robot was somehow lacking. I consider the way a robot looks to be equally important as what it does. No human will want to closely engage with an unappealing robot. The appearance of my robot, however, had largely been left to the discretion of an industrial designer. Was that a good decision? Would that really guarantee an optimal design? I certainly did not think so. Of course, this designer had produced a plan based on many years of personal experience, along with consideration of other products manufactured throughout the world, but I was working on a new kind of robot— one that was to interact with human beings—so there was little precedent to work from.

We robot researchers have come to unquestioningly accept what are considered "robotlike" designs, despite their coming from persons with no expertise in this new field. I considered this to be a highly significant problem. As I mentioned above, form and function have equal importance in robots that will interact with people. After all, isn't that the case with automobiles? The price tag on a Ferrari, for instance, clearly isn't based on either performance or appearance alone. If performance were the only issue, why would so many people want a Ferrari in a country like Japan, where the highest legal speed limit is 120 kilometers per hour? Clearly the way the car looks is part of its appeal. Appearance—in other words, design—is extremely important for all industrial products. What I wanted to know was, why hadn't anyone sought a scientific basis for such designs?

Indeed, what is the ultimate design for a daily-life robot? When robot technologies have advanced as far as we can take them, what kind of robots will we want to use? The remainder of this book attempts to answer these questions. The following pages explain how I approach them and preview the answers that I have come up with.

The human form is the ultimate form

Humans are extremely sensitive to humanlike forms. Even as we walk down a busy street, we immediately distinguish people from other objects around us. Indeed, many studies in the field of neuroscience have shown that our brains are wired for this sensitivity to the human form. In a sense, human brains are designed to recognize other humans. We also tend to anthropomorphize machines and tools. For example, we might have a conversation with the kettle as we brew ourselves a cup of tea, and in doing so, we would unconsciously decide what parts were its nose and its mouth and so on, giving it a face. Our brains exist largely for interacting with other people, to the extent that we search for humanity in the objects we use. It therefore makes sense to consider the human form to be the ultimate design for a robot.

Most previously developed robots do reflect human bodies to some extent. Not only do they often have two arms and two legs, mimicking the primary features of the human body, but they also often have a somewhat humanlike face. However, possibly due to preconceptions that robots ought to be different from humans, our anthropomorphizing is typically limited, leaving them clearly not human.

My big question was, why do robots have to look like robots? Conversely, why have we made them look only somewhat human up till now?

In fact, while scientists generally accept that our brains are designed to recognize other humans, there have been no careful investigations into the extent to which we should humanize our humanlike creations, such as robots. I was convinced that this appearance issue should not be left to industrial designers; it called for in-depth study by researchers. Having arrived at this conclusion, in 2000 I started studying androids.

Perhaps jumping from appearance straight to androids seems extreme, but I felt this was the more logical of two possible approaches. One would be to start with a very simple robot and gradually make it more humanlike. The other would be to start with an extremely humanlike robot—in other words, an android—and carefully whittle away any unnecessary features. Regarding the former approach, I had no idea how many robots I would need to build before arriving at my end goal, nor how to start crafting them. The latter approach at least provided a clear initial goal: to create the most humanlike robot I could. I therefore took this path.

Women and children first

The first android I made was a robotic child. I did so because it would be similar in size to other robots I had developed, better allowing me to use them for comparison when investigating the importance of a humanlike appearance. I named this android "Repliee R1" and modeled it after my daughter.

The Repliee R1, based on a child model, developed at Osaka University.

16

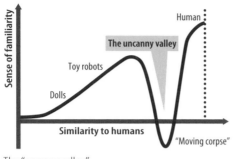

The "uncanny valley"

The chart labels: Sense of familiarity (vertical axis), Similarity to humans (horizontal axis), Human, The uncanny valley, Toy robots, Dolls, "Moving corpse"

However, cramming all the mechanisms required to mimic human motion into a package the size of a child's body was not possible. This is crucial because even if it has a perfectly humanlike appearance, an android that moves awkwardly looks very creepy, almost like a zombie. This phenomenon is called the "uncanny valley." Namely, the more humanlike a robot's appearance, the more important it is for its motions to be humanlike too, to avoid making its viewers uneasy.

The term "uncanny valley" was coined by Mori Masahiro, formerly a professor at the Tokyo Institute of Technology. The graph above shows this valley, with sense of familiarity on the vertical axis and the robot's appearance on the horizontal axis, moving from simplest to most humanlike. When a robot's appearance becomes very close to that of a human's, sense of familiarity suddenly drops, giving it an uncanny appearance. The main cause of this is believed to be an imbalance between natural appearance and movements.

To replicate the natural human movement required to escape the uncanny valley, I needed to make an adult-sized robot capable of housing the required complex mechanisms. My next android thus looked like an adult woman.

This android, the "Repliee Q2," had forty-two actuators (devices used to realize body movements) in its upper torso, allowing it to move in a very natural, humanlike manner. In addition to typical neck and arm movements, the android performed motions that humans make unconsciously, such as eye movements and the shoulder movements that accompany breathing. Repliee Q2 used pneumatic actuators, a mechanism like a syringe that extends or contracts using injected air, somewhat like a simple artificial muscle. Robots generally use electric motors. However, these motors require gears for braking, which creates an extremely non-humanlike noise. I used pneumatic actuators to avoid this noise.

They had another advantage as well. It is difficult to apply external power to operate electric motors with geared braking. With air actuators, however, we can adjust air-pressure levels to smoothly provide a strong external force, just like with an electric motor. The result is movement highly similar to that produced by human muscles. Pneumatic actuators do have drawbacks, though. For one, highly precise motion

The Repliee Q2, based on an adult female model, a joint development project between Osaka University and Kokoro Company, Ltd.

through pneumatic control is extremely difficult, so these actuators are not well suited to the kind of accurate and speedy motions seen in factory robots with electric motors. Also, while the only device needed in addition to an electric motor is its battery, pneumatic equipment tends to be quite large, because the actuators require compressors to deliver compressed air. Indeed, the compressors required to operate the forty-two actuators that drive Repliee Q2 take up more space than the android itself. This means an android using pneumatic actuators to move cannot walk.

Even so, through a combination of a humanlike form, humanlike movements, and the kind of sensor network needed for a daily-life robot, Repliee Q2 produces a very humanlike image. My research team presented this robot at Expo 2005 in Aichi prefecture to great acclaim. The international media in particular took great interest, and selected Repliee Q2 as the best of the specially exhibited robots there.

2

REMOTELY CONTROLLED ANDROIDS

Creating a new self

Our presentation of Repliee Q2 at Expo 2005 was a success, but visitors clearly wanted more. Repliee Q2 was able to recognize people and have very limited conversations. Specifically, it could offer a greeting and then make a comment or two about the Expo. Several visitors were dissatisfied, however; they wanted to extend their conversation, and wanted to know why Q2 couldn't talk about other topics.

It will be no simple task to create an android that can autonomously converse with humans. It may even turn out to be impossible. Truly humanlike conversation will require artificial intelligence equivalent to a human brain, and we are nowhere near realizing that kind of technology. Even so, this is the ultimate goal of robotics research.

In any case, I now had a direction to head in with my next android. I would aim not for autonomous conversation but instead for an android that could engage in conversations through remote control, similar to the daily-life robot I had created before. The system would include the android and a remote-control system. Because this was a new kind of robot, I gave it a new name: the "Geminoid HI-1." This name of course comes from *gemini*, Latin for "twins" (as in the constellation), an apt name since I modeled this android after myself.

The Geminoid HI-1 (right), developed at ATR Intelligent Robotics and Communication Laboratories. (Photo by Ishida Makoto)

Incidentally, the term "robot" can refer to anything that uses sensors to detect its environment, a computer to make decisions, and motors or other actuators to move. In that sense, even some air conditioners and cellular phones can be considered robots. Robots that are clearly not human but have some elements of a humanlike body, such as a head and limbs, are called "humanoids." Humanoids like Geminoid with a very humanlike appearance are called "androids."

Like Repliee Q2, Geminoid HI-1 has features allowing it to reproduce humanlike movements. Specifically, from a sitting position it can autonomously make motions resembling human respiration and eye movement. The computer controlling Geminoid connects to the Internet, allowing it to be controlled by a remote operator. Operations are very simple. The operator needs only a laptop computer, which displays images from two cameras installed near Geminoid while the operator converses with people speaking to it. The operator's voice is captured using a microphone, sent to Geminoid via the Internet, and played from speakers installed behind it.

One of the two cameras is used to observe Geminoid, the other to view the person speaking with it. A camera installed on the controlling computer captures the operator's face and uses image processing technologies to model head and lip movements. The system sends this information to Geminoid in real time, allowing it to mimic lip motions in sync with the voice played through the speakers. Geminoid similarly mimics the operator's head movements.

Arm and other bodily movements are controlled via an operations panel on the computer screen. For example, a "bow" button causes Geminoid to bow when pressed. There is a reason I designed the system this way rather than having the android mimic every operator motion it can, which is of course technically possible. Geminoid is not capable of all human motions; it can only move

The author, remotely operating a Geminoid.

its arms and head from a sitting position. Therefore, if Geminoid were designed to automatically duplicate all of the operator's motions to the extent possible, the operator would be limited to motions Geminoid is capable of, which would be very constricting. Using buttons to instruct Geminoid to perform bodily actions allows the operator to move freely and concentrate only on head and lip motions.

I noticed one very interesting thing about Geminoid. After operating it to converse with visitors for some time, Geminoid starts to feel like an extension of my own body. I can see Geminoid's lip and head movements on the computer screen, and looking at the monitor feels nearly like looking in a mirror. Put another way, using Geminoid's body allows a form of telepresence, existence at a remote location.

Creating another female android

Developing Geminoid HI-1 and testing it out in various places opened my eyes to its potential. At the same time, these experiences showed me that HI-1 was highly over-engineered.

Geminoid allowed users to project themselves at remote locations, providing them and those with whom they interact with a sense of presence different from what we experience when teleconferencing. Users could directly speak and interact with others at remote locations, as if they were truly there. Teleconferencing allows us to send images and audio, but that is not enough to provide a true sense of presence. We simply feel as if we are speaking with someone far away who is projected on a monitor. This is a very different experience from speaking with someone right in front of you. Geminoid, however, is a physical presence that looks identical to its creator. It can even be touched. This is quite unlike an image on a screen.

When I was first building HI-1, it was not clear how much of a human-like appearance was needed to produce this effect. I thus made the most complex robot possible. However, a few years of use revealed that not all of Geminoid HI-1's functions were necessary.

Drawing on this experience, I created "Geminoid F," a simpler remotely controlled android with the minimum set of functions needed. As with HI-1, it would allow users to project their presence to remote locations via computer-based remote control, and to converse with people there. However, it would do so with the least possible functionality.

While Geminoid HI-1 had 53 "degrees of freedom" (roughly, the number of actuators), Geminoid F had only 12. Specifically, three actuators allowed up–down, left–right, and diagonal head movements, one produced a bowing motion, 1 mim-

The minimally functional Geminoid F, a joint development project between Osaka University and ATR Intelligent Robotics and Communication Laboratories.

icked respiration, two realized right–left and up–down eye movements, one was for blinking, two created smiles and frowns, one moved the android's eyebrows, and one opened and closed its mouth. While HI-1 could move its arms and legs, F could not.

I also greatly simplified the system. Because HI-1 had so many degrees of freedom, it required a 200-volt compressor larger than Geminoid itself. The devices used to control airflow were also large, approximately half the size of Geminoid's body. Of course, it also needed a computer to control its operations. In contrast, because Geminoid F had only twelve degrees of freedom, it could be operated using a 100-volt home-use compressor approximately the size of a chair. Further, since Geminoid F had no actuators in its legs or torso, we were able to use those spaces to house the equipment for controlling airflow.

Situating control equipment within the android's body had an additional benefit. This equipment produces some amount of heat, which when coming from within resembles body heat. Geminoid F's limbs and torso were thus slightly warm to the touch, making it even more lifelike.

I incorporated one new technology in Geminoid F: its smile. I do not smile much myself, so I did not think to include this expression when creating Geminoid HI-1. For Geminoid F, however, I went to great lengths to reproduce a pleasant smile. Doing so allowed me to create a much more natural, attractive expression.

Limiting the functional design to what was absolutely necessary also greatly reduced production costs. An identical android could be created for less than US$100,000. I wanted Geminoid F to be used in society at large rather than to serve as a new research platform, so reducing production cost was very important. If Geminoid could not be used in a wide variety of situations, it would not validate the goals of my research. Manufacturing costs therefore had to be low enough to place the end product within reach of researchers, hospitals, and other potential users.

To make Geminoid F more internationally acceptable, I modeled it on a Japanese woman with one Russian grandparent. I learned this lesson while field testing Geminoid HI-1 in Austria in 2009. Since I would be repeating my experiments in more situations and countries, I decided it would be better to model it on a woman who could be viewed as either Japanese or non-Japanese instead of on a typical Japanese male like myself.

Choosing models

I have created many Geminoids and other androids, and I have always chosen my models very carefully. I always ask myself why they are suited to my objectives for that particular android and why I should choose this model over all others.

When creating my child android, Repliee R1, I wanted it to measure between 100 and 120 centimeters tall to allow comparison with the appearance of robots designed by industrial designers for daily-life situations, like Wakamaru (developed by Mitsubishi Heavy Industries) and my own Robovie. This is why I chose a child as a model. I used my own child due to the rigors of the manufacturing process. Creating an android that looks exactly like a human being requires not only taking photographs from every possible angle but also creating a full-body mold so that even the skin can be perfectly replicated. Making this mold involves covering the entire body in plaster similar to what dentists use for tooth molds, a hard thing to ask others to subject their children to.

When developing my adult female android, Repliee Q1, my objective was to reproduce natural humanlike motion, so the face did not need to look exactly

The Repliee Q1, designed to have an "average face," a joint development project between Osaka University and Kokoro Company, Ltd.

like any specific individual. I therefore referenced the "average face" determined by the Japanese Academy of Facial Studies. This face was based on average values from the faces of thirty-one women from around the world. As it turns out, "average faces" are quite attractive. Several factors relate to whether a face is considered attractive, one of which is its symmetry. An average face naturally exhibits symmetry. Actually, an average face erases any outstanding characteristics, making even gender somewhat ambiguous. Perhaps this lack of remarkable features strikes us as attractive; interestingly, it is also slightly inhuman.

I needed an adult-sized body to reproduce natural motions, but why a woman? Because I wanted to show the completed android to a large number of people and conduct experiments to confirm how humanlike it appeared. I felt a female would be better received by viewers, particularly children who could be frightened by a male robot. This is why I made my first adult android female.

The next android I created, also female, was the "Repliee Q1 Expo." The goal of this android was to display fully autonomous operation at Expo 2005 in Aichi prefecture. A secondary goal was to test whether a face based on an adult human model would make the android feel more human. I asked NHK newscaster Fujii Ayako to serve as our model because she appeared on television every day and was likely familiar to many Japanese visitors. Repliee Q1 Expo thus became the first android based on a public figure.

When you are duplicated as an android, somebody, somewhere is always looking at or fiddling with a copy of you, and I worried that this might create some degree of psychological burden on the duplicated person. Since Ms. Fujii was a professional newscaster used to being seen on television, I hoped the public attention would not bother her.

As a condition of using her likeness, she specified that the android could only be used for media coverage of Expo 2005 and research related to the Expo project. Once the Expo was complete, therefore, we gave Repliee Q1 Expo a new face, turning it into Repliee Q2. Beyond a new hairstyle and eye shape, there was no fundamental difference between these two androids. That was enough to make Q2 look completely different, however. Changing the eye shape in particular had a large effect; our eyes appear to express our human individuality very directly.

The android I built after Repliee Q2 was my remote-controlled android, Geminoid HI-1, which I modeled after myself for the following

reasons. First, I wanted to try creating an android with a male body. The slim build of the female androids I had created before restricted the number and functionality of actuators I could use. I wanted the freedom of a larger body to see if I couldn't create an android with smoother movements. Also, I wanted Geminoid HI-1 to allow users to send their presence to other locations. By modeling this android on myself, I could send it in my place to represent me. Even when giving presentations overseas, I could send

The Repliee Q1 Expo, based on a newscaster, a joint development project between Osaka University and Kokoro Company, Ltd.

Geminoid and avoid the troubles of a long airplane flight and jet lag.

But my primary reason for modeling Geminoid after myself was that I wanted to know how it felt to have a robotic doppelgänger. The models for my previous androids were quite surprised when they first met those creations. Neither, however, was able to clearly describe the experience in terms sufficient for academic inquiry. To understand what they felt with greater precision, I needed to experience having my own look-alike android.

The android I made after Geminoid HI-1 was Geminoid F. I developed this android with the goal of being able to use it in more practical settings, meaning the android had to be less expensive and more general-purpose. My appearance tends to frighten children, so it is inappropriate for broad application. I therefore used another female model for Geminoid F. I also knew that expressions like smiles and frowns help human viewers become more deeply involved in conversation with an android. I therefore chose a model who could express an attractive smile and a clear frown. I was considering use of this android in hospitals. Specifically, I wanted this android to accompany patients during medical examinations, nodding along with them to provide a sense of security. I also imagined these robots serving as conversation partners for those undergoing long hospital stays. In the end, I used a woman working in the medical field as my model, under the condition that I would not reveal her personal details.

I will return to this subject of android appearances later in the book, but before doing so, in the next chapter I would like to pause to consider what a world filled with Geminoid-type androids might look like.

A WORLD OF SURROGATES

The post-Geminoid world

So far I have described the background of Geminoid's development, but allow me to set aside discussion of its technical aspects for now to imagine a world in which Geminoids are commonplace. We'll get back to development in the next chapter.

Actually, an excellent illustration already exists of what a Geminoid-filled world would look like: a 2009 movie called *Surrogates*. This film was released in the same year as *Avatar*, which you are more likely to remember. Both are science fiction films. *Avatar* depicts the use of remotely controlled bioengineered beings on another planet, while *Surrogates* takes place on the Earth of the near future.

To give a simple description of the world of *Surrogates*, robotics technology has greatly advanced, and highly humanlike androids have been developed. Technologies for controlling robots through brain–machine interfaces have also been perfected. Combining these technologies has resulted in "surrogates," namely androids that users can mentally control to conduct their daily lives. Humans can thus remain safe in their homes, using special equipment to remotely control their surrogates working outside. Through these robotic surrogates, users are able to

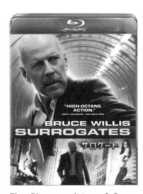

explore remote locations as if they were actually there, and even experience what it is like to have superhuman athletic abilities.

This is exactly the kind of world that widespread adoption of Geminoids could realize. In fact, my look-alike Geminoid and I make an appearance in *Surrogates*; the film opens with a brief documentary of sorts showing advances in robotics technology over the years, at the end of which we are presented as the culmination of these advancements. The fictional movie then begins.

The Blu-ray edition of *Surrogates*. (© 2014 Buena Vista Home Entertainment Inc., released in Japan by Walt Disney Studios Japan)

Life with surrogates

Unlike *Avatar*, I felt that *Surrogates* raised many questions pertaining to actual human society. The entire film is like a very realistic thought experiment. It was not a huge box-office hit because it lacked *Avatar*'s production budget and extensive marketing campaign, but in terms of technical content related to human life in the near future, it is much more thought-provoking than *Avatar*.

A bit more about the film: actual surrogates can be purchased at shops resembling cell phone stores, and just like nearly everyone today has a cell phone, nearly everyone in mainstream society has a surrogate. Since surrogates are such a pervasive commodity, there are shops selling them on every corner. A shop is always handy should a user wish to repair a broken surrogate or upgrade to a better model.

Surrogates are androids, so they do not age. Buyers must therefore decide how old their surrogate will look at the time of purchase. Nearly all surrogates in the film are adults; there are no children or elderly people. I assume this reflects people's tendency to choose the point in their lives they feel best represents them.

Of course, this is a movie, so the plot is somewhat extreme in places. For example, it ends with the destruction of all surrogates, which strains credibility. Just as the Internet we use today cannot simply be "turned off," we will not in the future create a system of androids so fragile that it can be destroyed by taking down some central server that controls them all. I wished the plot had instead involved a system crash that made it impossible to know who was controlling which surrogate, which seems more within the realm of possibility.

Melodramatic Hollywood storytelling aside, I truly enjoyed the film's depiction of a future filled with remote-controlled androids, and the challenges that society and individuals might face in such a future.

Androids are becoming a reality in the US

You may think that robotic surrogates will forever remain in the domain of science fiction. But in fact, the seeds of their creation have already been planted. Just in the past few years in the United States, researchers have made great strides toward creating remotely controlled robots capable of completing everyday tasks.

The remote-controlled mobile robots we have today are extremely simple. Most are only slightly larger than the popular cleaning robot Roomba. Many of these robots support a monitor displaying the tele-conferencing software Skype, positioned slightly below human line-of-sight. Remote operators open a Skype window on their own computer, allowing them to converse with people in front of the robot, which they control with a joystick.

I presented exactly this idea at the International Conference on Intelligent Robots and Systems in 2000. My proposal did not attract much attention at the time, but today it is becoming reality in the US. Indeed, I have heard that hundreds of such robots are already in use.

For example, they are being used in some American hospitals to facilitate consultations by specialists in distant locations, or to allow family visits in situations where a face-to-face meeting would be dangerous.

The telemedicine robot Vita, developed by InTouch Technologies, Inc.

Telepresence robots also allow specialists to attend surgeries taking place far away. While the use of telepresence robots to actually perform surgeries remains rare, these robots allow direct observation and participation by doctors who otherwise would not be able to attend due to time or travel constraints. Medical practice is becoming increasingly specialized, and the use of telepresence robots will likely be necessary in the future to allow highly specialized doctors to treat patients worldwide.

Remote-controlled robots are popping

up in other contexts as well. I once attended a meeting at a Silicon Valley robotics startup called Willow Garage. One of the attendees was a robot. More precisely, a Texas-based software engineer named Dallas attended the meeting via robot. The day's agenda included progress reports by team members and a group discussion of future research, so attending via robot posed no barriers for Dallas's participation. He was able to move freely about the room and speak with others as needed.

As a software engineer, Dallas was able to work at home so long as he could take part in the occasional meeting. The robot enabled him to live anywhere in the world without sacrificing his career. Indeed, when we met he was living in rural Texas while working at a company in California. Instead of paying Silicon Valley's sky-high real estate prices, he used his Silicon Valley salary to purchase a large house in a rural area where the cost of living was dramatically lower. Lifestyles like this will likely become increasingly common in industries where it is possible.

But I wondered, was Dallas satisfied with his simplistic robot? Wouldn't he rather have a body that allowed him greater freedom of movement, or even remote sensations? The bare minimum functionality needed for his job might be a fine start, but surely he would prefer a more humanlike body that enabled freer work.

During our meeting, I intentionally got in the way of the robot Dallas was using. I even jostled it about. When I did so, Dallas reported that he felt like I was doing these things to him. In other words, the feeling of inhabiting Geminoid that I got after using it for an extended time occurs even if the robot doesn't look at all human.

In a past study, a researcher operated my daily-life robot Robovie by remote control for over one month while working on a co-

The Texai Remote Presence System, developed by Willow Garage.

operative research project with a team in the United States. He reported a similar phenomenon: the more he used the robot, the more it started to feel like his own body. Of course, neither Robovie nor the robot that Dallas used could move its lips or head in sync with its operator like Geminoid could. Those robots simply used a speaker to relay the operator's voice. They could, however, move wherever their operators directed them. So while they could not represent their operators' body motions like Geminoid could, when operators used them for long periods of time as surrogates, they experienced the sensation of the robot becoming an extension of their own body. However, the process happened more quickly with a highly humanoid, motion-duplicating android like Geminoid.

"You look a lot like your synth"

Let us return to *Surrogates* for a moment. Among its many interesting scenes was one depicting a beauty salon specifically for surrogates (which the movie also refers to as "synths"). By contrast, the movie showed no beauty salons for humans. People generally remained in their rooms and did not even show their true form to family members, so what would be the point of dressing up? The appearance of one's surrogate—that is, one's actual interface with society—was far more important.

This scene caused me to rethink what a surrogate would mean to its owner. Specifically, I wondered if they would function as extensions of cosmetics. Many women I know refuse to go outside without makeup. Because they feel their made-up self is their true self, interacting with society without makeup on does not feel right. It is not too difficult to imagine that makeup becoming thicker and thicker until it forms a mask, and then the mask to start behaving autonomously as a surrogate. Surrogates would thus become essential for life within society.

This is precisely what happens to the wife of the protagonist in *Surrogates*. Speaking to her surrogate, the protagonist tells her that he wants to know the "real" her. I found this bit of dialogue very interesting. No doubt the protagonist is questioning the nature of human identity. Which is his true wife? The surrogate, or the unadorned, aging woman who operates it?

In a separate scene, one character tells another, "You look a lot like your synth." See the subtle mistake there? Shouldn't that be "Your synth looks like you"? After all, surrogates are fashioned after human beings. Saying "you look like your synth" flips that around so that the surrogate becomes the basis for comparison. The speaker is recognizing the surrogate as the true person in a social context.

I've seen this happen myself. When I was developing Geminoid at ATR, the director often said to me, "You're starting to resemble Geminoid." My answer was always, "That's impossible—Geminoid is starting to look like me," but the director wasn't the only one; others at ATR made similar comments. This is evidence that Geminoid was taking on my identity.

The dictionary defines "identity" as "who or what a person or thing is." In other words, given an android and the model on which it is based, identity from a third-party perspective lies in whichever others recognize as the individual. In my case, those at the ATR laboratories viewed Geminoid rather than my flesh-and-blood self as hosting my identity.

Clues that people use to determine someone's identity include characteristics like the person's title or important achievements. In fact, as I will discuss in detail in a later chapter, we have little interest in those from whom all such characteristics have been stripped.

The real you

As I mentioned above, *Surrogates* does a much better job than *Avatar* of making viewers think about fundamental questions such as the essence of human identity and the "self" as viewed by society.

Technological advances have allowed us to remove various restrictions from our environments as we steadily produce machines that take the place of human abilities. For example, we now use automobiles to move from place to place, machines to wash our dishes, and even robots to vacuum our floors. Indeed, the history of technological development is one of machines replacing human workers. By freeing us from physical constraints, technology has altered the definition of humanity. Consider how much more difficult it was for society to accommodate disabled persons two or three hundred years ago. Thanks to technological progress, however, today far fewer handicaps preclude full participation in society. While a disabled person may still encounter challenges, their lives are much more similar to those of the non-disabled.

Our physical bodies no longer define us. If we lose an arm or a leg, it can be replaced by a prosthetic. Research is rapidly advancing on various artificial organs, and further progress will allow replacement of increasingly many body parts with mechanical devices. Surely society will accept even those whose bodies have been almost entirely replaced with machines as human. Geminoid and the androids in *Surrogates* represent the extreme of this freedom from our bodies. I have no doubt that society will eventually recognize this type of remotely operated robot as human.

This of course raises a question: if we aren't our bodies, then what are we? In the near future, it may become possible to replace our bodies with machines. Not in a literal sense, perhaps, since transplanting our brains into a robotic body would be very difficult, but if we can someday use our brains to directly control remote machines, the end effect would be the same. It would be impossible to distinguish between a remotely controlled mechanical body and one that can autonomously perform decision-making and actions. In other words, from the perspective of those around us, the machines would be us.

But can a remotely controlled robot fully embody an individual human being? One could certainly argue that the answer is "no," since a remotely controlled robot is simply moving in response to commands originating in the human brain operating it. However, such remote operations will gradually be automated. For example, it is relatively easy for machines to perform greetings and other simple human interactions, even using today's technology. In the future, commands produced by the operator's human brain will gradually come to be produced by the machines themselves. Such technological progress will further blur the distinction between what is human and what is mechanical.

This will no doubt make defining humanity even more difficult. However, progress—and indeed, living as a human being in the truest sense of the word—has always challenged us in that way. Throughout history, technology has replaced various functions of the human body with machines. As that happened, those functions came to be regarded as superfluous to defining humanity. Yet each new discovery also deepened that definition because it demonstrated that we are more than our bodies. I believe that pursuing this deeper understanding is the raison d'être for beings that evolve through technology, and the true meaning of human life.

Answering the question "what is humanity?" is too difficult for any one person, given our limited context of ourselves and those surrounding us. We should instead begin with a simpler question: "What am I?" By describing my experiences developing androids and how they affected my thoughts regarding this question, I hope to provide you with opportunities for thinking about your own identity.

I do not mean to imply that I have settled on an answer as to what I am, or what my true nature is. If nothing else, however, I have determined that it is not my body that defines me. I have further found that identity varies with place and time, making it incredibly difficult to grasp. Within "me" is a self that writes books, a self that designs robots, a self that tends toward a sense of superiority when giving lectures ... and many other selves. Those who engage with multiple forums on the Internet likely contain even more selves. Can we really select one of these aspects as our "true" self? Do we really have only one true self?

While I have questions about exactly *where* such a self might exist, I have no doubt that it (or they) *does* exist. I feel and am conscious of it. What I want to know is the nature of a self that is aware of, but incapable of truly grasping itself. What is a human that believes itself to be human?

Perhaps "I" is just a convenient word we use when we need to distinguish between the self and other aspects of society, meaningless beyond that. Maybe my belief that some true self exists behind the word "I" is simply a delusion. As I will discuss later, the same may be true for the human "soul." After all, the soul, too, has no physical aspect, so perhaps our belief that it exists is unfounded. That certainly sounds like the correct answer, philosophically speaking.

Even so, I cannot believe this without confirming it for myself, and one path to doing so is to create an android that looks identical to me. My experiences and those of others involved in android development have been extraordinarily thought-provoking in this respect. While I cannot give readers these same experiences, my hope is that by describing them in this book I can provide some opportunity for reflecting on what "human" and "self" might mean.

4

BECOMING AN ANDROID

Questioning MRI

Androids have taught me many things, both through the process of their creation and afterwards. In this chapter, I describe what the female model for Geminoid F and I felt during the fabrication of our look-alike androids, along with what we came to understand about ourselves and humanity. I also discuss the gender-related differences in our perspectives as models. This gender difference, too, provides interesting insights into the nature of humanity.

Creating an android based on a human model involves a number of preparatory stages. First, we take many photographs of the model from all angles in both standing and sitting positions. These photographs are our most vital resource when fabricating the android and finishing it off to look exactly like its model.

We also perform both internal and external scans. The internal scans are MRI images, cross-sectional photographs of the model's entire body. Images of the model's skull are particularly important. The android's head must contain a skull shaped exactly like the model's so that the silicone skin covering it will faithfully reproduce a human head. If the skull is not properly shaped, the skin will be loose over the head in places, and feel very strange when touched.

Both the female model and I underwent MRI imaging of our skulls. I did not find the process particularly unpleasant, but I recall feeling very strange upon seeing the resulting images of my brain and skull. In a word, I was in a state of disbelief. I spent around an hour in the MRI machine, and immediately after I got out, the technician presented a stack of photographs, saying, "Here's your brain." There was also a set

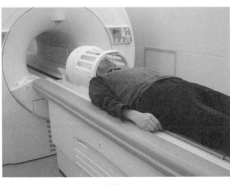

The author, undergoing MRI imaging.

of computer files containing images taken at various depths. Using a dedicated image display program, I could browse through those snapshots to view whatever cross-sections of my head I wished.

However, I found it impossible to truly connect those photographs with my actual brain. The profile of course looked like my own, so I was able to recognize myself in those MRI images. But cross-sectional photographs erase all personal characteristics, making it impossible for me to see myself in them no matter how many I looked at. Photographs taken with a normal camera capture familiar bodily characteristics that reassure you they really do depict you. I found no such assurance in MRI images.

I even found my thoughts becoming borderline paranoid. What if I had not a brain but a computer in my head, and the MRI technicians had given me someone else's images to protect me from the shock of that discovery? It was particularly eerie to think of this mysterious stuff they told me was my brain as being crammed into my skull. I thought that if my skull suddenly turned transparent, allowing my brain to be externally visible, I could never step outside again.

We humans are hardly aware of the organs contained within our bodies. We are not completely oblivious, of course; drink a cup of hot tea and you will feel the heat in your belly, allowing you to truly sense that there is a stomach within your body. We almost never have an opportunity to feel most other organs, however, particularly the brain. We also lack any way to directly sense its odd form.

Although we have a good sense of the surface features of our bodies, our insides remain somewhat mysterious. As might be expected, when thinking about what we truly are, we typically do not extend consideration to our body's interior. We humans have a highly superficial concept of ourselves. What kind of being does that make us?

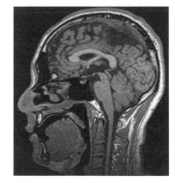

"Here's your brain."

Awareness of the "I" within

One thing my MRI images gave me was an assurance that "I" am a collection of sensory organs situated at the border between my body's interior and exterior, and in the end I can only feel things inside and outside my body through these surface-layer senses. In other words, I do not perceive myself throughout my entire body. Regardless of what our body contains, even if it were filled with artificial objects like machines or computers, we would not be cognizant of that. A self-aware human being—an "I"—is thus nothing more than a collection of surface-layer sensors such as skin, eyes and ears. "I" am a fragile array of sensations.

In any case, these are the thoughts I had as a result of seeing my MRI images. My experience was a little different, however, when I watched the photo shoot of the model for Geminoid F.

Watching someone else undergo an MRI scan allowed me to observe the scans gradually appear from a third-person perspective. This left no room for doubt that they might be counterfeits. Even so, there was something unreal about watching the internal structure of someone's body appear before me, something very unlike seeing the model herself. Honestly, I did not feel I was seeing an actual human being; I almost felt I was watching an alien being scanned.

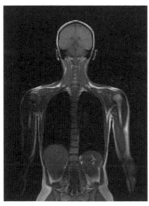

An MRI image of the Geminoid F model.

We are so used to seeing only the exterior of other human beings that their internal structure can appear almost inhuman. Given that, it doesn't really matter what's inside us. If, for example, the Geminoid F model's MRI scan showed her to be filled with robotic mechanisms, I imagine I would still interact with her in the same way after the scan was complete. "Hey, looks like you're a robot on the inside," I might say.

An MRI scan allows us to see the full form of the subject's body in every detail.

In other words, we can see the person exactly as they are, even deep within their body. This is useful for android development, because the form of the spine is particularly important when determining a robot's posture. As I watched the model being scanned, I wondered what she was feeling, and particularly whether she found the process embarrassing. Before I relate her comments on the subject, however, I will return to my feelings when seeing my own MRI images.

In my case, I was possessed by a strong sense of mission to create my android, and the MRI was merely a means to that end. Even so, I admit to being slightly embarrassed when I saw the results. For example, MRI images show exactly how much fat is in your body, and where. It is embarrassing for others to see how poorly you are taking care of yourself. Clothing goes a long way toward concealing such unappealing aspects of ourselves, but there's no hiding from MRI. I also learned that sagging skin and other imperfections appear much more starkly than we are used to seeing. In fact, the only kind of person likely to be completely unembarrassed by their own MRI would be a bodybuilder with a low body fat ratio. Someone with a normal build taking a peek beneath their skin would see much more fat and decline than expected.

I was concerned enough on viewing my MRI images that I asked the doctor if he saw anything I should be worried about. I mentioned that I had once hurt my back, so he took a look at my lower spine and said, "Ah yes, you have a slight stenosis of an intervertebral disc here," pointing at exactly where I still felt pain. Looking at the MRI while thinking about how the physical characteristics shown there cause me back pain had the effect of reconfirming that the images before me indeed depicted my own body.

MRI today is still expensive and time-consuming, but what if it became dramatically simpler? What if viewing MRI images was as easy as looking at yourself in the mirror each morning? It is certainly conceivable that someday in the near future, you will be able to use a home MRI device to investigate every pain and twinge. What would such a future teach us about our bodies? Rather than recognizing ourselves merely by the external, skin-covered appearance we normally see, perhaps we would learn to recognize ourselves by the assembly of our bones, the form of our muscles, and the locations of our fat deposits. Maybe this technological advancement would expand our sense of self to include the interior of our bodies. If that happened, it would be an instance of a new technology evolving our sensory functions and changing how we regard ourselves.

Turning back to the model for Geminoid F, like me she found it difficult to recognize her MRI images as her own body. She told me that by looking carefully at her profile in the images she could pick out details that were similar to her body and recognize herself that way, but she felt no connection to the images of her body's interior. She even said the body depicted there seemed to belong to no one at all, so she didn't feel embarrassed about people seeing it despite MRI being something like ultimate nakedness. I got the impression that I was more embarrassed by the experience than she was.

She also said she hadn't realized how complex her insides were. I fully agreed. Indeed, the complexity of the human body is difficult to imagine. Even taking just our arms and legs and the muscles that move them, that system is so complex it seems miraculous we can control it. This is one reason we are largely unconscious of the organs and muscles within us; constant conscious control would entail far too high a cognitive burden. Our inner self is thus not even a stranger, it is something more distant and formless. It is impossible for us to look at our body's interior and find "self" there.

Looking at my MRI images, I recalled another movie: a 1999 film called *Bicentennial Man*. In this film, Robin Williams plays an android, originally designed as a housekeeping robot, that somehow discovers creativity and a wish to become human. It eventually obtains a human-identical appearance, but during the modification process it glimpses itself in a mirror with its face removed and is shocked by what it sees. I found this highly relatable. If we do succeed in creating androids with humanlike abilities, I believe they would be as surprised as humans are to see what they look like on the inside.

The self we see, the self others see

As I mentioned before, creating an android based on a human starts with photographing the model from all angles. One of our goals with Geminoid F was to reproduce a broader range of facial expressions, so we photographed its model smiling, frowning, and making other expressions. We found that the expressions most natural to humans that can easily be reproduced by an android are smiles and frowns, so we selected one photograph of the model making each face. We also used a three-dimensional scanner to scan and measure the model while she made those same faces, allowing us to create a computer graphics model. This second step is important because photographs alone are insufficient for accurately recreating a face. To do so, I had the model look back and forth between her photo and a mirror to help her make the same expression, which she maintained for two or three minutes as the scan was complete.

At least, that was the original plan. As it turned out, I had overlooked a major problem: reflections in mirrors are horizontally reversed, but faces in photographs are not. This may seem like a minor issue, but in fact it is quite difficult to mimic a reversed face. I therefore displayed a flipped image on a computer so the model could directly compare it with her image in the mirror. Everyone involved in this task noticed another interesting fact: horizontally flipped images of faces give different impressions. A researcher once told me that one image in the pair would appear more

3D imaging of a facial expression.

masculine and the other more feminine, meaning a gender bias exists between photographs and mirror images. I was not sure whether the Geminoid F model's photographs were masculine or feminine, but they clearly looked different from her mirror image.

This raises the interesting question of which face we most easily recognize as our own. Both the Geminoid F model and I felt that the face in the mirror was the most familiar, while that in the photograph felt somehow strange. In other words, we recognize as "self" our mirrored image, a perspective no one else ever sees, while others are more familiar with our photographed image, which we find odd. There is thus a gap between our own image of self and others' perception of us, and from the other's perspective our image is wrong. From that perspective, we lead our daily lives under a slight misconception about ourselves.

I asked the model what she thought about her reflected and photographed images. She told me that the photograph showed her public face, while the mirror showed her true self. She also said that the face in the

Horizontally flipped images of the Geminoid F model. (Above: photograph; below: mirror image)

mirror was the self she wanted to be. On the other hand, while the face in the photograph was definitely hers, it was not the one she aimed at when fixing her hair and putting on her makeup. This implies that the face she worked so hard to create through application of makeup was not the face that others see; she applied makeup without ever knowing how society saw her. Further, she put on makeup more for herself than for others. The more I thought about it, the stranger it seemed.

Photographs are, from the

start, transformations of ourselves. I wonder if those who desire self-transformation enjoy being photographed more than other people do. The self we see in a photograph is different from the one we see in the mirror, and when we talk about that photographed self with others, there is some degree of misunderstanding in the conversation.

I sometimes also wonder what it would be like to have a mirror that reflects how others see us. In fact, something like that is available: a "true" mirror that reflects in a way to show us a non-reversed image. Looking into such a mirror and seeing a self that is slightly different from what we are accustomed to is a peculiar experience. These mirrors cannot be used like normal mirrors; when trying to touch one side of your face, your first instinct is to raise the wrong hand.

So which type of mirror is more natural for humans? There are many mirror-like things around us. We can see our reflection in still water and in windowpanes, for example. Possibly not only humans but animals, too, naturally use mirrors. However, all mirrors in the natural world flip their reflections; none shows the viewer the image that others see, like a "true" mirror does. In that sense, the inability to accurately recognize ourselves is not a product of social life but rather is embedded in the natural world from the start. Any life form that is able to recognize itself thus lives without an accurate picture of what that self is.

I believe that this lack of accurate self-perception is in fact essential to life as a social animal. Since we humans can only know our true selves through others, we must act socially. Perhaps one reason we and many other animals form societies is to attain accurate self-perception.

My meditations on mirrors have led me to believe that human sociality has inevitably arisen in close association with the natural world. If we are to create robots (or even computer simulations) with humanlike sociality, we must do so based on this mirror concept. Doing so may explain the origins of human sociality in ways that previous research could not.

Creating expressions

For me, one of the most challenging aspects of developing androids has always been creating expressions. My reason for developing them in the first place is to investigate the importance of a humanlike appearance, but a "humanlike appearance" comprises many factors.

The first conundrum I encountered when I started studying androids was whether it was better to copy actual humans or design new unique faces. If I based my research on an android that looked exactly like one specific human, that person would function within my research as something like a representative of all humans. I would thus want the model for the android to be a very "average" person.

For this reason, when I created my first adult android, Repliee Q1, I referenced an average face as determined by the Japan Academy of Facial Studies. The impression it created when completed, however, was vaguely non-human. Creating a sufficiently humanlike robot is a basic premise of android research, but I found that an android with an "average face" looked artificially fabricated. I therefore used the NHK newscaster Fujii Ayako as the model for my next android, Repliee Q2.

Repliee Q2 was far more humanlike than the Q1. Indeed, it looked exactly like Ms. Fujii. The same was true for me and my Geminoid HI-1 android, and for the Geminoid F and its model. This convinced me that modeling androids on specific individuals works far better than using a half-baked "average" face. We do not yet have techniques for selecting the individual components that make up a truly humanlike face. We do not know what characteristics of human facial features are sufficient for expressing humanity. This unsolved problem offers an intriguing area for research.

One approach might be to use rapid prototyping machines—computerized devices that produce three-dimensional objects from sets of two-dimensional images—to generate a variety of faces. One might make precise three-dimensional measurements of a model's face, read that data into a computer, create models of various faces with features gradually removed, then use a rapid prototyping machine to instantly create the actual android. However, making a humanlike face takes more than reproducing a humanlike shape. Expressions in particular are very important, and the motion of skin over the face must look natural. Facial shape and skin movement cannot be considered separately.

Human faces create very different impressions depending on the angle at which they are viewed. We have replicated this in androids. A face photographed looking slightly downward appears sad, for example. This is true for the Geminoid androids as well, because they look so real.

Small changes in expression, such as a shift in gaze direction, also impact the impression human faces give, sometimes significantly. However, such changes in expression do not result in a loss of humanlike appearance. At times they even emphasize humanlike qualities. As of today, no research into humanlike characteristics has considered changes in expression, indicating the complexity of human faces and their expressions, and the profundity of what constitutes a humanlike appearance.

The extent of such changes likely changes from individual to individual. When creating my look-alike Geminoid HI-1 android, I focused mainly on how I furrow my eyebrows, because everyone I asked pointed that out as my most characteristic expression. One of the staff at ATR labs is skilled at drawing caricatures, and the one she drew of me was very simple, showing just a pair of glasses and furrowed eyebrows. Even so, anyone who saw it—myself included—knew it was a picture of me.

I do not remember thinking much about other expressions when creating that android. My goal was to make the most complex, realistic android possible, so I did include very fine actuators capable of producing smiles and some other expressions. However, the resulting android could not smile as well as I had hoped.

I don't think of myself as someone who is frequently emotional. I rarely get angry, and when I do my anger passes quickly, because I don't consider anger a very useful emotion. It makes me hungry, prevents me from focusing on my work, and is not an enjoyable state to be in. Not getting angry is therefore the best policy. I also avoid excessive joy. This may be why many of the people I work with, students in particular, are frightened of me. I've even seen particularly timid students tremble while talking with me—not because I'm angry, but simply because I have a scary appearance. The same thing happens in the course of my daily life. I rarely get bad service, either in Japan or overseas. I think this is because I look scary at a glance, so service providers do their best to avoid displeasing me.

The flipside of this lack of extreme emotion is my paucity of expression. This expressionlessness may even be what makes my android look so much like me. In light of the previous discussion, you might say I do not have a very humanlike appearance. My acquaintances have made this quite apparent of late, often jokingly asking whether I am myself or one of my androids. At least, it started out as a joke when I created Geminoid HI-1. But it continues today, five years later, so I suppose something about me must be very android-like. This is a reminder that appearance can, and likely does, reveal character. I suspect my expressionless face betrays close to ninety percent of my personality.

In contrast to myself, the model for Geminoid F was very attractive. Even so, her expressionless face can be quite scary. She works in the medical field and mentioned that she sometimes frightened small children. Possibly for this reason, she smiled frequently. She had a very nice smile and likely took pains to maintain it. In other words, her "scary" and "happy" expressions were both extremely clear.

When trying to make Geminoid HI-1 as humanlike as possible, I focused more on its face than on the expressions it could make. In that sense, I was possibly its best possible model. In contrast, I worked hard on Geminoid F's expressions, despite my goal of simplifying its mechanisms to reduce production cost. I was stepping away from a humanness with an unchanging expression toward a humanness with varying expressions.

For Geminoid F, we devised a way to effectively generate expressions while keeping the mechanisms involved as simple as possible. We included an actuator so that the android could furrow its eyebrows, allowing it to produce expressions from a narrowing of the eyes into a frightening stare to a clear display of disgust. We also embedded actuators that slightly raise its cheeks along the laugh line to pull the corners of its mouth into a smile. In previous androids I had included as many actuators as possi-

A Geminoid frowning and smiling.

ble, referencing the layout of human facial muscles, so that they might reproduce any expression, but Geminoid F used a small number of actuators dedicated to specific expressions, allowing it to very clearly produce those expressions. The android's skin is made from silicone, which lacks the flexibility of human skin and therefore limits expressiveness somewhat. Even so, I find Geminoid F's expressions much more realistic than those of Repliee Q2 or Geminoid HI-1.

The embarrassment of our inner workings

After creating the mold for an android's body, then creating its skin and designing its mechanisms, we assemble those mechanisms and cover the body with the skin, which must then be painted. Actually, after assembling the mechanisms and just before applying the skin, we once again compare the android with its model for some final adjustments. Adjusting the space between the eyes is particularly important because this powerfully influences our impression of a face.

Seeing the internal mechanisms before they are covered with skin is extremely valuable for the android's model. It is almost like having your real inner self exposed before you. Considering that this android will soon look exactly like you, the experience is similar to looking inside your own body. Despite being robotic, the mechanisms already bear features you can clearly recognize as your own. One example is the eyes, which are

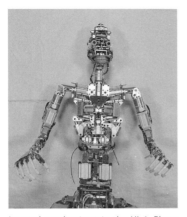

Internal mechanisms in the HI-1. Photo courtesy of ATR. (Intelligent Robotics and Communication Laboratories)

specially made by a prosthetics designer to look exactly like yours. The same holds for the teeth, which are faithfully reproduced in rigid silicone based on a mold taken by a dentist. All coloration is also true to life, based on color samples. It is primarily the eyes and teeth that cause you to recognize yourself, but other parts give hints, too, if closely observed. Once you see it, the mechanisms before you clearly represent your inner structure.

This contrasts strongly with viewing your own MRI images, which are quite terrifying to consider as showing your own body—so creepy, in fact, that it's hard to look at them for very long. With the android, however, while some parts like its eyes and mouth are on vivid display, these are parts that we can see in our own body any time we wish. Other parts of the android are filled with beautiful aluminum mechanisms, so there's nothing particularly bothersome about viewing them. It's quite a strange sensation. So if I were to choose between the two, I'd rather look at the robotic body than my own MRI scan.

I asked the Geminoid F model how she felt about the experience. She told me that while she'd said her MRI wasn't particularly embarrassing, in fact some parts were, such as images from below her waist. She said she found her android with its inner workings exposed embarrassing in a similar way. Even though she was looking at robotic mechanisms, they were clearly made in the form of her own body, so when viewed in total it was like seeing her own body exposed.

An interesting factor in creating the interior mechanisms for Geminoid F was that its model had a much worse posture than most people. When most people sit up straight in a chair, their ears are positioned directly over their shoulders, but the F model's ears were far forward from that position. When she stretched her back to look straight ahead, she bent backward. I noticed this when photographing her before fabricating the android. I asked the model whether she wanted her android to look like this too, or if I should correct her sitting posture. She requested the latter, saying that perhaps by seeing herself (in the form of her android) sitting with better posture, she might make efforts to correct this in herself.

Internal mechanisms of the Geminoid F.

That makes sense to me. Seeing someone who looks just like you but without an obvious defect might provide a clear goal for self-improvement. I wonder, however, how long one might pursue such a goal. As I've discussed before, we humans are not particularly good at recognizing ourselves, and view even androids that look exactly like us as strangers. Even if our android looks exactly like us on the surface, we won't in fact recognize it as being exactly the same.

That being said, I noticed that the F model had a much better posture within less than half a year. Today, when she sits down her ears naturally come directly over her shoulders.

Which is the most attractive: face, clothing, or hair?

After making final adjustments to the android's mechanisms, the skin gets attached. At this point, the android still doesn't have hair, and its skin is the color of raw silicone, which makes for a very poor complexion. Although the android's profile clearly resembles your own, it still evokes no strong feeling of looking at your double.

Then a movie makeup artist steps in and has the model pose while applying makeup to the android. The eyes take the longest. Eyelashes must be implanted and special care taken to get the coloring around the eyes just right. It is fascinating to watch the android gradually come to look more like you over the course of the day or so it takes to complete the job.

The android looks most like you just before it receives hair and clothing. This was true for both Geminoid HI-1 and F. Perhaps this is because subtle changes in hairstyles and clothing greatly affect our impressions of a person. Further, we can easily change these aspects of ourselves on a whim. This makes them less important for determining what makes a person look like him or herself. When trying to discern who is in front of us, we discard these easy-to-change factors.

Even so, hairstyles and clothing quickly draw our attention, and everyone considers these to be important parts of making ourselves look appealing to others. I myself take note of the hairstyles and clothing of people I meet. In other words, the elements we use to make ourselves attractive are separate from those that represent our individuality. So when men and women look at each other, and particularly when a man looks at a woman, which is he looking at? It's difficult to imagine feeling attracted to someone without taking their hair and clothing into consideration. Would the beauty of a bald woman with a pretty face be enough to make a man feel attracted to her? Every now and again, movies feature beautiful actresses with shaved heads. I wonder how attractive viewers find those women. Personally, I usually have a hard time telling whether someone with a well-formed face but no hair is male or female.

My sense is that roughly speaking, it is hairstyles, clothing, and cosmetics—decorations added to our bodies—that others find attractive, not our unadorned appearance. In other words, I do not believe our features are primarily what attracts others. We are like peacocks, displaying our feathers to appear beautiful.

I asked the female model how she felt watching as her Geminoid was completed. She said that as its silicone skin was added, its eyelashes implanted, and its skin colored, she increasingly felt like she was standing next to someone that looked a lot like her. At some point, she said, it didn't just look like her, it looked prettier than her. The first reason she gave for this was that unlike human skin, silicone skin is perfect, without any of the wrinkles or imperfections we all develop. She added that she envied its glow.

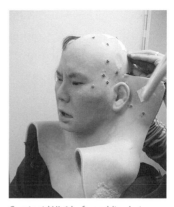

Geminoid HI-1 before adding hair.

Perfect skin isn't the only thing that makes androids look a little inhuman. The best way I can describe the other factor is to say that they're somehow juvenile. They have the same aura of innocence, purity, and naiveté as a baby or a young child. I didn't think about that while creating Geminoid HI-1, but when comparing Geminoid F and its model side-by-side and hearing the model's comments, I could understand the sentiment.

She made another interesting comment: "I want to become more like an android." Perhaps some people idealize pure, childlike qualities and find androids to be an embodiment of that ideal.

The finishing touch: clothing

Once the android's body is complete, the finishing touch is to put clothes on it.

Selecting clothing for Geminoid HI-1 was not an issue, because I've been wearing the same clothes for nearly twenty years. (Not to imply that I haven't changed clothes for two decades; I have several sets of the same outfit.) In fact, I'm often asked why I wear the same black clothes every day, to which I reply, "Why do you feel like you have to wear different clothes every day?" There are questions on both sides here. The people around me want to know why I always dress the same, when everyone else wears something different every day. They want to know why I'm different from everyone else. Conversely, I question the importance of varying outfits.

Perhaps it is an idiosyncrasy of researchers to be annoyed by things that lack logical justification. In terms of clothing, I first felt this annoyance with regards to neckties. All men in Japan wear ties at work and in other semiformal situations. But why? I can't think of a good reason for it. We Japanese have attire suited to formal situations: kimonos. Jackets and neckties are British culture, not Japanese. Why do we unquestioningly bring aspects of another culture into situations calling for formal dress?

Kimonos are admittedly difficult to move in. If the claim is that we started adopting Western clothing in the Meiji era because it allows freer movement, I say we should have done a better job at adapting it to Japan. Clothing is important because it characterizes a country's culture. Kimonos may be constricting, but suit jackets aren't exactly highly functional either. They have large collars with no apparent function; they can't even be turned up against the cold. Neckties are even more baffling. What's the point in hanging something that looks like a thin towel from your neck?

I first joined adult society as an associate professor at the University of Yamanashi. After starting work at the university, I only wore ties in situations where people would get angry with me if I didn't. Today I never wear them. If they're meant to make your throat more attractive, there are better ways of doing that. Without going too deep into the details, I created a small device that keeps my shirt collars stiff and properly arranged. In formal situations, I use this device in place of a tie pin. It attaches to both lapels rather than clipping to a necktie, and prevents them from spreading out. I keep it nicely polished to look attractive. I think it looks much better than a piece of cloth wrapped around my neck, at least.

There's another reason why I don't wear many different outfits: clothing is sometimes more prominent than facial features. When you see someone from far off, you notice their outfit first. You start paying attention to their face only when they come closer, and only when they are standing right in front of you can you ask their name. In other words, clothing makes the strongest first impression in terms of identity. It strikes me as logical that just as we do not frequently change our names or our faces, we should not frequently change what we wear.

That being said, maintaining the same wardrobe for two decades has been no simple task. Since purchasing twenty years' worth of trousers and shirts with exactly the same design wouldn't have been realistic, I settled on black non-pleated slacks and standard business shirts, which I believe will be manufactured forever.

There are several reasons why I settled on black. For one, it is the most convenient and functional color. I can wear it to both weddings and funerals. I can even head to one straight from work. It is functional in winter because it is the color that best absorbs heat. I also chose black because of my name; the "guro" in "Ishiguro" means "black," and this overlap between my habitual color and my name strengthens my identity. I sometimes wonder how my name came to be "Ishiguro," but I've decided that post hoc reasoning is sufficient to answer that. I'm Ishiguro because I wear black.

Viewed from this perspective, our clothing, faces, and names all affect our development over time. Stand in front of someone you know and recall their name. You will soon realize it is part of what has made that person him or herself. Names and clothes influence how we grow up, making these an important part of how our personalities form. If you doubt this, try dressing in a single color like I do for half a year and see what happens.

If possible, I would like everything I wear to be made-to-order, or even made by my own hands. Making clothes and satchels should be nothing compared to building a robot, after all. If I had the time I would do so, but unfortunately I want to do too many things, and must do too many others, to devote that much effort to my appearance. I do sometimes make small items between writing papers and working on projects. I am quite proficient at making leather cell phone cases and keyholders, for example, if not with millimeter precision. Unfortunately, cell phone models update frequently and I tend to be an early adopter, so I have trouble keeping up with homemade cases.

I sometimes think about what the ideal clothing would be, and one answer I've come up with is the *Star Trek* uniform. I've heard that many people, both Japanese and non-Japanese, think those uniforms look like onesie pajamas. From the perspective of a *Star Trek* fan, though, they are ideal—functional and unadorned. I truly believe that clothing like that worn by the *Enterprise* crew will become popular in the near future. I don't think the fashion industry is doing a very good job of producing truly innovative clothing. There's too much adherence to traditional designs and customs. Then again, jeans became and remain quite fashionable, and they are highly functional, so there's a plausible chance that *Star Trek* uniforms will come into vogue as well. I look forward to that day. I'm going to get a black one.

I've gotten far off track here, but my initial point was that to dress Geminoid HI-1, all I had to do was bring in a shirt and a pair of trousers like I always wear from home. Things weren't so easy with Geminoid F, however. She didn't wear the same outfit every day, nor could I expect her to, no matter how convenient that would be.

One of my key objectives in developing Geminoid F was to use it in hospitals. In my experiments, therefore, it would be wearing a white nurse's uniform. When using it for other purposes, however, like a media event I describe below, I needed to choose more suitable attire. I had to ask myself what the most appropriate outfit would be for Geminoid F as an android.

The issue of attire was particularly problematic when we first introduced Geminoid F to the press. Having developed a new type of android for use in everyday situations, we held a media event to present it. How do you dress an android for a situation like that? I discussed the question at length with a manager at Kokoro, the company that fabricated Geminoid F, but in the end we decided to leave it up to Koshino Junko, a fashion designer known for her robot-inspired pieces. We had heard she was highly interested in our android, so the Kokoro manager, the Geminoid F model, and I went to meet with her. She immediately grasped what we were after and agreed to work with us. Clothing selection started that very day.

Her first proposal was one of her well-known pieces, a dress that looks like a futuristic hoop skirt. However, while it was a very interesting outfit to model while standing up, it wasn't suited to an android that would always be seated. I liked the idea of having Geminoid F and its model wear the same robotic clothing, but we had to abandon this design.

Ms. Koshino's next proposal was a formal black piece decorated in silver and gold. She also had a men's outfit in the same line, which she offered to lend me for our media event. Unfortunately, when the female model and I stood next to each other wearing the same get-up, we looked like a pair of down-and-out entertainers. The Kokoro manager said we looked good, possibly in deference to Ms. Koshino and her staff, but I had my doubts. I emailed him a photograph of the model and me together and demanded to know what he really thought. "To be honest," he replied, "I can't stop laughing."

The problem, of course, was not Ms. Koshino's design, which looked fine in the studio. I even tried on the suit she had lent me and thought I didn't look too shabby in the mirror. I soon came to my senses, however, and realized how strange I would look in any other context. The photo we took together sealed the deal.

High fashion requires the right setting, lighting, and photographic techniques to look good. The circumstances in which such clothing is worn can make the difference between stylish and foolish. This was particularly true for me, as someone with a normally unvarying wardrobe. Casual clothing is most natural for casual circumstances, and formal clothing is best for formal situations. This is another reason why I don't wear neckties, and have settled on an outfit that can be considered as either casual or formal.

In any case, I decided that I shouldn't wear the same outfit as Geminoid F and its model when we had our media event. In the end, F and its model wore the same outfit in different color schemes. Both were basi-

60

The media event, with matching outfits. Geminoid F is on the left.

cally black, but Geminoid F's had a dusting of silver, while the model's was gold. The silver has a somewhat inorganic feel, making F appear more robotic. I was very pleased with how the two of them looked sitting side-by-side at the event, and very thankful for Ms. Koshino's talent. While Geminoid F and its model looked exactly the same, their highly refined fashion helped to bring out something unique in the presence of both. Upon seeing the dressed-up android, its model once again said, "My android is prettier than I am. I want to become a human who is equally attractive and pure. It's like looking at my ideal self."

Ms. Koshino's outfits are very expensive, so we could only borrow them for the day. This meant we needed to dress Geminoid F in normal clothing the next day. This time, I decided to let the model pick the outfit, asking her to choose whatever she thought looked best. She selected a black dress, which is what Geminoid F still wears today. When I asked her why she chose black, she said it has a slimming effect and is suited to the most situations.

I had both Geminoid F and its model wear this dress, and again asked the model what she thought. She said that while she thought it looked good on her, the android might look better in another color, possibly some shade of blue or aqua. I suppose clothing must be selected based not only on one's looks but on their overall aura. I also realized that what one wears emphasizes not only appearance but also mood and even personality. I asked the model if she wanted us to choose a different outfit, but she declined, saying she'd prefer to keep wearing the same thing as Geminoid F. Possibly this was related to her wanting to become more like her android.

When robotics research has advanced to the point where androids can make their own decisions, I wonder what kind of clothing they will choose. (Naturally, I also wonder if they will change their outfit every day.) What kind of appearance will androids choose for themselves? I'm not sure at what stage in human development we become concerned with our appearance. When humans and robots begin to have social relationships, the question of how androids choose their appearance will likely become a very interesting area of research.

The other me

Simply put, having an android that looks just like you feels somewhat similar to having another you exist right in front of you. I will close this chapter with a discussion of the psychology of this experience.

The first sight of your completed Geminoid is a very curious experience. At first, the unmoving Geminoid looks something like a wax figure, which makes it a lot like a mirror. However, it is different in three ways. First, it doesn't move at all, while a mirror image follows your every movement. Second, a Geminoid is horizontally flipped from what you expect, since we're used to seeing and identifying ourselves as a mirror image. For this reason, a Geminoid doesn't look quite like you. It's recognizable, of course, but a certain something marks it as slightly off. Rather than looking in the mirror, it would be more accurate to say it feels like looking at your twin.

The third difference is that you can see parts of yourself that aren't visible in a mirror. For example, you normally cannot see the back of your own head. Exploring the unfamiliar back of a head with my face attached to it felt like belatedly discovering new parts of myself. In my case this was no great surprise, but it certainly could be for someone who looks very different from behind than what they expect.

I was, however, surprised by my many faults. It made me think that perhaps I overestimate myself in everyday life when I assume all the unseen parts of my body look perfectly fine. Even after seeing this other self with all its flaws exposed, however, I still like my own body. Not that I consider myself a fine example of the human male, but we men tend to be quite optimistic and self-centered when it comes to our appearance.

In contrast, as I have described several times now, the Geminoid F model found that her "other self" represented her ideal, and therefore considered the android to have the better body. Again, not to hold her up as a representative of all women, but this might show that many women judge their appearance more harshly and less optimistically than men do.

Another difference is that the model for F saw her android as an opportunity for self-improvement. She said it would be interesting to use Geminoid F to model outfits she wasn't quite brave enough to wear herself, on the off chance that they might suit her better than expected. Similarly, she said she wished she could use Geminoid F to try out new hairstyles.

Having a second self presents any number of opportunities for trying new things. In particular, this other you can act more boldly, opening up new potential for you. When this second self, this android, is surrounded by other people, it leads a separate life from our own. When we use it as a guide for how we should behave and what we should become, we are able to learn not only through our own experiences, but through those of our android.

CHAPTER
5

ADAPTING TO GEMINOIDS

Like your own body

Once the android's body is finished, it must be combined with a remote operation system. This system allows users to feel as if they have relocated themselves into the android.

As I described before, operating a Geminoid is very simple; it's largely a matter of watching some computer monitors and pushing some buttons while you speak with people. After using Geminoid for a while, you start to feel like it's your own body, and those you're interacting with start to consider Geminoid to be you. I call this "adapting" to Geminoids.

This adaptation process takes some time. The longer you use one, the more it feels like your own body. This may follow a similar principle to that of the "surrogates" in the film I described in Chapter 3. When a Geminoid is used for a long time, it becomes less confusing for those interacting with it to simply view the Geminoid as its operator. Similarly, when surrounded by such people, it becomes easier for you to accept Geminoid as your own body.

I was curious to know how similar a Geminoid and its operator needed to be for adaptation to occur. Contrary to expectations, I found that when people other than myself operated Geminoid HI-1, those who knew me well could make it act more like myself than I could. I'm not well aware of my own habits, but those around me were highly conscious of them, and by intentionally reproducing them in their operations they created a very convincing impersonation.

Of course, if we improved the remote operation system to the point where the android precisely reproduced all operator movements, Geminoid could behave exactly as I do. However, it's difficult to reconcile Geminoid's seated posture with that of an operator staring at a computer screen, so those improvements will take some work. One problem will be particularly difficult to overcome: allowing both operator and android to perform the same movements while maintaining the same posture will require allowing the operator to view the android's environment through its eyes. Unfortunately, the images captured by a camera are very different from those viewed through human eyes. In particular, there is a significant difference in the width of the field of view. Overcoming this problem will likely require the operator to wear a head-mounted display with an extremely wide field of view. For the area

A girl in Austria operating a Geminoid.

around Geminoid to be viewed three-dimensionally, we will need to install cameras in its right and left eyes so as to separately present the captured images to the user's eyes.

In any event, operators need not be the Geminoid's model in order to convincingly operate it. When we displayed a Geminoid at a museum in Austria, we set up its remote-control system some distance away from the android. Interestingly, an elementary school student tried using the system and was able to do so more skillfully than most adults. A crowd gathered around the Geminoid she was operating, and she chatted with them with the skill of an actress for nearly an hour.

It has been five years since I developed Geminoid, and many people have operated it since then. Many have adapted to it, allowing them to use it as if it were their own body. Comparing male and female users, I found that women adapt to Geminoid far more easily. I suspect that this is because women are more used to slightly transforming themselves by changing their makeup and clothing. Even so, I was surprised to find that they were able to adapt so well to a Geminoid that duplicated my body. In fact, the person I first think of when recalling the most skilled Geminoid operators is a female secretary at my lab. Investigating what fundamental gender differences enable women to adapt more readily to Geminoid than men would likely make for some interesting research. I haven't found the time to look deeper into this myself, but I hope I will be able to do so in the near future.

One thing I have investigated, though, is whether a body as humanlike as Geminoid is required for remote operators to adapt to robots. The answer was a resounding "no."

For several years now, I've been conducting joint research with the University of Washington involving remote operations of my daily-life robot Robovie, which I described in a previous chapter. A professor of psychology there with an interest in robotics is studying how people react when a robot is present in the lab, acting as part of the research team.

Robovie is operated remotely, but not in the same way as Geminoid. For one, operators cannot use this robot to converse directly with others, because a human voice coming from a very non-human robot would be too jolting for those interacting with it. The robot's voice is therefore composed of synthetic sounds. The operator can select from a list of prerecorded phrases, or, when no appropriate selection is available, use a keyboard to type what the robot should say. A text-to-speech program converts this input to sound, allowing the robot to produce speech.

This study continued for three months and involved many subjects. I visited the lab at around the time the experiment was concluding, ostensibly to see how things were going, but I'll admit to an ulterior motive: I wanted to participate in the study myself. As when I visited the Palo Alto group, I was not a well-behaved participant—I intentionally got in the robot's way, and even gave it a few taps. Once again, the students who were operating the robot when I did so reported feeling as if these actions were happening to them.

Compared to a Geminoid, Robovie looks far less human. It doesn't even allow direct speech, relying instead on keyboard input to communicate. Even so, its users adapted to its body within three months of remote operations.

What, then, would happen with a robot whose actions were even further simplified? One of my current collaborators once conducted an experiment similar to that at the University of Washington. This was part of a very interesting study that investigated whether embedding speakers in everyday objects and causing them to "talk" would lead users to sense something human in them. For example, a desktop lamp might say something when the user reached to turn it off. The study found that this caused most people to hesitate before turning the lamp off, suggesting that they felt it contained a humanlike element.

When the experiment was repeated with a box, however, there was no such whiff of humanity. I suppose that's no surprise; a simple box playing a voice is little more than a speaker, and few people would hesitate before turning off a speaker. Even so, the main difference between a lamp and a speaker is that the former gives off light, which directly affects us. People sense humanity in this effect, minor though it may be, while they do not feel that from an inert box. Even if such a box produced a human voice, people would consider it a voice-playing tool with no hint of the humanness we see in robots. Somewhere around here is the borderline separating what we consider another intelligent being and what we consider simply a useful tool.

The important point is that given enough time, we humans can find humanity in a surprising range of objects. Further, the likely trigger for such adaptation is whether we perceive objects as exerting an influence on us. This demonstrates just how easily we humans adapt.

Attractive people and performers make the best operators

Allow me to return the discussion to Geminoids and what kind of person can most skillfully operate them.

At first, intuition told me that the best operator would be the Geminoid's model. However, that initial guess didn't last long after I finished Geminoid HI-1; as described above, I soon found that those around me, in particular a secretary who knew me well, did a far better job than I.

Things were slightly different for Geminoid F. The Geminoid F model operated her android far better than men could. This brought me back to my original hypothesis, that a Geminoid's model is its best operator. In fact, the model for Geminoid F was also a far better operator than most other women. I asked her why she thought that was the case, and she replied that since it looked exactly like her, she was invested in making it move naturally. When someone other than a Geminoid's model operates it, they tend to focus on talking with other people, without worrying much about its movements. In other words, they aren't very concerned with how the android is perceived.

Given that, it's possible that those who are most conscious of being seen make the best Geminoid operators. And who is most conscious of being seen? Attractive people, for one. Attractive people stand out, and are therefore likely to be sensitive to how people view them. This makes me suspect they pay more attention to their appearance. The Geminoid F model is one such person, but I don't know whether she was good at operating her android because it looked like her, or because she was used to people viewing her as an attractive person. Clarifying that would require creating a Geminoid modeled after someone that others and the model him or herself consider less attractive. I don't have any such plans at the moment, but I hope that if Geminoid research broadens, another researcher will take on this challenge.

Another candidate for most conscious of being seen is performers. Actors and actresses are constantly aware of how they are being viewed. To test this theory, I asked an actress who had participated in a "robot theater" featuring Wakamaru daily-life robots to operate a Geminoid. The results were surprising: she was even better at it than the model was. Apparently, similarity to an android is not particularly important in determining how skillfully its operator manipulates it; training related to how one is seen, like that which performers undergo, has a greater effect.

As in the case of the "android theater," which I'll describe in more detail in Chapter 8, this actress adapted well to Geminoid. Just as performers immerse themselves in their roles, she became fully immersed in Geminoid, an android that looked nothing like her.

As I reflected on this, I began to wonder which took precedence: acting ability that allows one person to become another, or being able to act like a person because you are that person. In my own case, reflecting on past experience makes me think I have worked hard at playing a role. For example, I'm sure many of my readers have experienced watching a movie featuring a cool actor, then walking out of the theater with something of his swagger. This is particularly common when we are in grade school, a time when we also tend to mimic those around us who we think are cool. Through imitation, we feel as if we have to some extent become that person.

This implies that our personalities form through our own choices. Personality is generally considered to form as a result of experience. Setting aside the basis for these claims, a closer look should show that in many cases personalities are self-selected. Further, I suspect that those who consciously make these selections have higher self-awareness, in terms of who they are, how they should be, who they look up to, and how they do not yet live up to the standards such idols set.

When I was a grade-school student, I often idolized my more popular friends. I almost never have feelings like that today, however, possibly because as an adult I have forged my own personality. In that sense, acting may be the profession through which we can best improve ourselves. Most would-be actors and actresses cannot make a living through performing alone; they must pursue their art while supporting themselves with a part-time job or whatnot. This lifestyle is very different from that of a student who, say, graduates from a university engineering department with a degree in robotics and takes a position at a private firm. I suppose aspiring entertainers pursue their art as a way of coming to better know and to improve themselves.

Even so, I believe there are limits to what one can learn while following such a path, because acting is only surface-level mimicry. For example, by playing the role of a daring doctor who saves someone's life, you might learn something about what doctors do. That does not, however, mean you've learned how to save someone's life. On rare occasions, I see news stories about how a highly regarded doctor was found to be practicing medicine without a license. For some doctors, perhaps a reassuring bed-side manner is more important than the medical techniques at their command, but this is the exception to the rule. Those techniques are the basis by which doctors earn their keep.

So what is it that keeps actors and actresses going even when they cannot find work? What do they expect to learn about themselves? They can learn about the various characters they play, but what use is that knowledge? By playing the role of a dying person, can one truly learn what it feels like to die? I've come to know several actors and actresses through the "robot theater" and "android theater" events I've been involved in, and always wished I could speak to them more regarding this point.

Certain techniques and behaviors make up what we call "a doctor," and by understanding these we can understand what a doctor is. In reality, however, no one doctor can acquire all of these techniques, and in any case, it is difficult to qualitatively and quantitatively measure them. Further, we would not call a new medical school graduate a "real" doctor. This makes me want to know all the more what it means to behave like a good doctor.

Second- and third-person viewpoints

Let's turn back to "adapting" to Geminoid. Regarding the factors that set the Geminoid F model and professional performers apart from other

Geminoid operators, we found that one difference is how closely they watch the close-up monitors showing the android's face. The remote-control system includes two monitors. One is primarily for watching the person conversing with the an-

An actress remotely operating Geminoid F while watching its expressions.

droid, but it also shows the Geminoid from behind so that the user can see the positional relation between the two. The other monitor shows a closeup of the Geminoid's face.

While the model and performers closely watched Geminoid's closeup, other operators focused on the other monitor, only rarely looking at Geminoid's face. This difference likely stems from the latter group's lower level of concern about their appearance. As a result, Geminoid sometimes moved unnaturally, and at times very strangely. The Geminoid system includes a computer that analyzes image data to recognize the user's movements, but it is necessary to watch Geminoid on the monitor to ensure that its lips and head are moving as expected. If not, users must take measures such as moving more slowly or opening their mouths a little wider. Since users who are less concerned about their appearance only rarely look at the monitor showing Geminoid's face, they do not notice that they are behaving in a way that prevents it from moving naturally, and therefore keep doing what they're doing. This phenomenon is of great interest to us researchers, specifically for what it reveals about the parts of our appearance we are concerned with when we interact with other people.

We see and are seen from three perspectives. In the first-person perspective, we view someone's face with our own eyes. In the second-person perspective, someone else looks at us. One of the Geminoid system's monitors shows this perspective. In the third-person perspective, both the Geminoid and whomever it is conversing with are shown on the other monitor.

I suspect that measuring the frequency with which an operator looks at each monitor when remotely controlling a Geminoid would tell us something about that person—that is, whether they are focused on their own appearance and thus consider the second-person perspective more important, or whether they focus on the expression of the person they are talking to, and thus value the first-person perspective. This might even make an interesting personality test.

I asked the model for Geminoid F what part of the android she most often watched while operating her android, and as expected she replied, "Its face." She added that she also watched the gaze of whomever she was talking to, so she could confirm through the video feed whether the android was making eye contact. She also told me she didn't worry much about watching the other person's face. More important than whether she is looking at the other person's face, she said, is that the Geminoid is.

Given that, I asked whether she thought she could operate a Geminoid that wasn't talking to anyone. She wasn't able to definitively say she could, and thought it would be hard to speak if no one was there to respond. Not only that, but "It would be so lonely if nobody else was there, like I had been abandoned."

The Geminoid homunculus

The phenomenon of adaptation has provided me with many ideas for further research. This is especially true because Geminoids present the possibility of performing experiments that in the past would have required human subjects.

Human experimentation has of course occurred throughout history. Experiments aimed at figuring out how our brains work are particularly interesting, but direct neural stimulation, typically performed during surgeries requiring a craniotomy, is so risky that it can only be done under extraordinary circumstances.

Thankfully, increasingly useful noninvasive techniques for brain function mapping now exist. I've already discussed MRI as a technology for producing images of brain topology; fMRI, an extension of that technology, can produce images of brain activity. Specifically, fMRI allows us to see what parts of the brain become active when specific tasks are performed. Another technology is optical topography, which uses light to monitor brain activity. When the brain is working it removes oxygen from the blood to produce energy (a surprisingly large amount of energy, in fact). Ascertaining where in the brain oxygen is being taken from blood tells us what brain areas are being activated. Light reflects differently off blood be-

fore and after this oxy-
gen loss, so changes in
reflection allow us to
track brain activity. As
you have likely seen
before, an MRI scan
requires placing the
subject in a large tube-
like structure. It also
requires the use of ex-
tremely powerful mag-

Remote operations with optical topography.

nets, which means subjects cannot have any metal objects on or within
their body. In contrast, the equipment required for optical topography is
highly compact, allowing measurement through a skullcap. There are
tradeoffs between the two approaches: unwieldy MRI equipment allows extremely detailed imaging throughout the brain, while optical
topography produces very low-resolution images at shallow depths. Both
methods are relevant to our discussion of how Geminoids might one day
replace humans in some brain experiments.

User adaptation to a Geminoid is in a sense similar to separating the
user's brain and body. This does not allow us to freely manipulate the user's
brain, but since the user's body is now an android, we have far greater
leeway in how we treat it. So while we cannot replicate experiments on
live human brains, we at least have more opportunities for performing
them on the body. My first idea regarding this was to create a map of
bodily sensitivity for Geminoids.

A brain region called the primary somatosensory cortex near the top
of the head connects to sensory regions throughout the body. One can
create a "sensory homunculus" map that represents the amount of space
in that area dedicated to receiving sensoy information from various body
parts. A three-dimensional representation of this map produces a very odd
figure, with prominently large lips and hands. This is because sensory

The "sensory homunculus" model of bodily sensations.

information from those locations registers across a relatively wide area in the primary somatosensory cortex, making them extremely sensitive.

My idea is to create something similar for Geminoids. Specifically, I would like to have the Geminoid F model or another skilled Geminoid operator who is well adapted to Geminoid F use a stick or some other implement to poke the Geminoid and find out how hard we have to stimulate what locations to cause operators to feel as if they have been touched. The experiments I have conducted so far are too preliminary to write up in a paper, but they hint at possible results: operators adapted to Geminoid F are most sensitive to stimulation of its cheeks, chest, and sides. It appears that stimulation of places on the android where we normally resist being touched or are most sensitive invoke a stronger sense of having been touched than do other body parts.

I suspect the sensory homunculus for a Geminoid will be unlike that for a human, with its exaggerated lips and hands. Whatever form it takes, it will likely be very interesting. Differing human and Geminoid sensory homunculi would suggest that the two have very different sensitivities across their bodies. If that's the case, and if robotics technologies advance to the point where humans are constantly controlling robots to conduct their daily lives, those people will be interacting with entities that are fundamentally different from themselves.

I suppose such homunculus experiments would be closer to robotics engineering than is my current research into how humans interact with remotely controlled robots, because they will require sensory information to be transmitted in a similar way as in human beings. When researching the sense of touch, for example, we might attach touch sensors to a robot, along with some device that transmits touch information to the hands of its operator, allowing the operator to feel what the robot feels.

However, I believe that so long as a Geminoid can successfully converse with another person, the brain of its human operator brain is able to supplement sensory input, even without extensive mechanical assistance from sensors or actuators. If it turns out that differences in how our brain supplements direct sensory input versus that from a Geminoid present some barrier to social activities when operating the android, a more engineered approach to remote control research may be required. One drawback to such an approach is that it will entail attaching many devices to operators while they control the android. This might interfere with the ability of operators to behave naturally when interacting with other people.

No one currently knows whether differences in sensory processing will be problematic, but whatever the case, investigating this issue will certainly make for some interesting research. It should lay the groundwork for creating sensory homunculi not just for Geminoids, but for any kind of robot. By partially incorporating robotics technologies for accurately transmitting sensory information, we can make whatever modifications to the sensory homunculus are needed.

In fact, after Geminoid F's model had operated it for a fairly long time and adapted to it, I asked a female staff member to touch the android in various places. I then asked the model to tell me which locations caused the strongest sense of being touched. The most sensitive areas were the android's lips, nose, armpits, and thighs. Runners-up were the chest, head, and stomach. She said she didn't feel anything in particular when its arms were touched, which makes sense given the operator cannot move the android's arms. Comparing sensory homunculi for humans and Geminoids, lip sensitivity is common between both, but there is little overlap otherwise.

This experiment involved only the F model, so it would be premature to draw any conclusions, but it certainly appears that there are big differences between body–brain connections within a human and those between Geminoid F and its operator. Senses in a human body connect to the brain via nerves, while in the case of a remotely controlled android, the android's body and the operator's brain are connected through vision. This seems to make quite a difference.

Operated operators

I can imagine many other experiments utilizing Geminoid adaptation, but as a second example, let us consider the sensations an operator feels when a Geminoid's body moves.

When using a Geminoid immobilized in a sitting position, operators start to feel increasingly constricted. This occurs because while its lips and head move during conversations, its body cannot. In other words, the operator feels Geminoid's physical constraints. I therefore wondered what would happen if Geminoid were moved through controls on another terminal, irrespective of the operator's intent.

Just imagining that scenario suggests interesting results. For example, should Geminoid's hand suddenly rise without the operator issuing a command, the operator might feel as if his or her arm had been lifted up. Alternately, if a head that had been operating smoothly suddenly made a large turn to one side, operators might feel as if something was wrong with their neck. A common trope in science fiction movies is an android being taken over by someone with malicious intent, who causes it to do something it isn't supposed to do. This would be a similar situation.

Many people might think of science fiction movies as nothing but made-up stories unrelated to actual research and development. In truth, however, imagination is the source of new technologies, so in that sense science fiction is a valuable resource. Researchers and technicians first dream up what they would like to accomplish, then consider how to turn those dreams into reality. An android able to host another consciousness was pure science fiction not long ago, but with Geminoid, we've taken the first step toward making such a thing possible. I believe technology has the potential to create a world where we can accomplish anything we can imagine.

In humans, the brain and body are not clearly distinguished, and the two can be connected as tightly as needed. Earlier, I wrote that operators are able to adapt to Geminoid because the brain and body are not closely connected, but I do not claim that they are completely separate. We feel that our brain monitors our entire body, even parts that are not densely connected through nerves; in reality, the brain sends and receives only information that is absolutely necessary. Put another way, our hardware does not include dense wiring throughout our entire body, but we have predictive software that allows us to skillfully use that hardware under the impression that we have dense wiring everywhere. Of course, debate regarding this issue is all within my own imagination, and nothing about it has been scientifically proven. However, I don't believe I'm far off the mark.

A Geminoid like the one I've developed might one day be used to improve its operator's motor skills. Say there's some action the operator wants to skillfully perform, but can't quite manage. In that case, a third party could externally manipulate the Geminoid to show that the motion is possible. Once the operator learned to make Geminoid perform the motion, they would theoretically gain the ability to do it themselves as well. In the case of Geminoid F, only the operator's lip, eye, and head movements are passed on to the android, but that is actually a lot to work with. For example, a user who didn't feel comfortable smiling or struggled with the appropriate timing for smiles during a conversation might practice using Geminoid F.

Operating androids to recall memories

When you've forgotten something and want to remember it, it sometimes helps to return to the place you were at when you were thinking about the now-forgotten piece of information, and repeat the actions you performed at that time. I've done that several times in the past. It works because human memories are often recorded along with memories of motion, as indicated by the fact that when we try to remember something, the motor areas of the brain become highly activated. I suspect that Geminoid holds significant potential as a memory recollection device if we take advantage of this characteristic of human memory.

For example, say a user has operated a Geminoid at work for around a week, and all of its motions have been logged on a computer. Further assume that the user has had several ideas during that week. The user remembers having thought of something at the beginning of the week—not specifically what, but approximately when. To help recall the idea, the operator could use the Geminoid to reproduce the movements performed on that day. Doing so could very well jog their memory.

CHAPTER
6

RELATIONSHIPS WITH GEMINOIDS

Our experiment in Austria

This chapter focuses not on Geminoids themselves, but on the relationships that arise between their operators and those who converse with them.

Our first experiments outside of the lab using Geminoid HI-1, the android that looks like me, took place at the 2009 Ars Electronica festival in Linz, Austria. We not only exhibited the Geminoid there, we also placed it at a table inside a café to observe how people responded to it. I think around half of the patrons didn't even notice it, walking right past without a glance. The other half sensed something odd and moved in for a closer look. After overcoming their initial hesitation, they were able to have a normal conversation and even become friendly with the android.

This is quite an interesting phenomenon. In essence, a Geminoid is like a giant cell phone that allows me to talk to people via the Internet from Japan. In some ways, however, it is quite different from a normal cell phone. For one, no one gives you evil looks for using it in a café. Speaking with a Geminoid appears similar to talking directly to another person, so even if the end effect is fundamentally the same as using a phone, doing so doesn't bother people in the vicinity, nor did it make me feel like I was imposing on others by making them speak to me under those circumstances.

This makes Geminoid an excellent tool for speaking with people in crowded places like trains and restaurants, where one might hesitate to use a cell phone. Talking on a cell phone is akin to muttering to yourself, which inevitably draws attention, but the effect is lessened when the conversation is mediated by a "person" sitting right in front of you. I'm not entirely sure why this is, but regardless, people seem to accept Geminoid as an in-person conversation partner.

That was what we observed at the café, at least. This experiment in Austria yielded other valuable insights as well. While operating Geminoid for three weeks I was able to speak with various people, which led to numerous discoveries. Allow me to relate some of the more interesting episodes.

We had to send a technician along with Geminoid for on-site maintenance. Including the preparatory period, he was there for around a month. This trip to Austria was his first major assignment, and while

Geminoid HI-1 in an Austrian café.

he knew some of the staff at a museum where Geminoid was displayed, he basically had to spend that month away from people he was close to. Especially considering that he hadn't been married for very long, a month of eating meals alone must have been a very lonely experience.

Possibly for this reason, he always seemed thrilled when I spoke to him from Japan via Geminoid. Not only did he have few acquaintances nearby, he was also surrounded by German speakers, making communication difficult; I think that speaking to and simply spending time with a familiar figure who spoke his language put him at ease. Several times he told me how happy it made him. I tend to frighten my students, if not my coworkers, but he was a rare exception; he wasn't scared of me even when he was my student, so we were able to interact on friendly terms.

He was happy to speak with me at any time, but I figured eating alone must have been particularly lonely, so I proposed that we have lunch together. Geminoids of course do not eat, but I suggested that he set the Geminoid up at his table during a meal so we could sit together and talk while he ate. After something of a wait, his very Austrian lunch arrived. I asked him about what he was eating, if it tasted good, and other things like that. He told me it was delicious and boasted of all the interesting things he had learned in Austria. Considering how thrilled he was to speak with my Geminoid, I think he might have cried if it had been his wife's Geminoid instead.

Café staff talking with the Geminoid.

About a week after we started our experiment, I met another person who really needed a Geminoid: a German student who came to assist from a university we'd worked with before. Her role was to speak with the Geminoid so we could compare how people reacted when it was apparently working on a laptop in a corner of the café versus when it was conversing with someone.

Like the technician, this student didn't know anyone in the area and was likely quite isolated. Like him, she told us that eating alone every day was very lonely. They ate together sometimes, but he was usually busy maintaining the android, so he often couldn't make the time. I therefore had several Geminoid-mediated meals with her, and she, too, told me it was a lot of fun. This experience cannot be replicated using a simple cell phone.

In Japan, many businesspeople are sent for extended assignments far from home, and I've heard that it's common for them to use Skype as a way to virtually have dinner with their family. I imagine that using a Geminoid instead would provide a much stronger impression of the person being there in the room. Teleconferencing applications give the impression of peeking through a window into the room where the other person is located, but they don't reproduce the feeling of being right there with them. With a Geminoid, however, one feels very much like they are right there.

Emotions communicate better than words

Having been modeled after me, Geminoid HI-1 is not very good at using facial expressions to communicate emotion. Geminoid F, however, was designed to reproduce a very beautiful smile. That smile makes a big difference in how others accept the Geminoid. A constant smile is considered an important part of service industry work for specifically this reason. People are much happier when speaking to a smiling face, even if that face belongs to an android.

Initially, I wasn't particularly interested in such issues, so I didn't realize the effect a smiling face would have. Something that happened during the media event announcing Geminoid F's creation opened my eyes, however. After I gave an overview of F's development and our goals, we had the model operate her android to introduce itself. This allowed the press to direct questions not only to me, but to Geminoid F itself.

When speaking with the reporters, Geminoid F was able to look directly at whomever had posed the question, smiling and nodding as she answered. She told me that she wasn't intentionally doing so at first, but that she noticed how this caused the reporters to smile and nod in return. This made her very happy, so she made a point of smiling at everyone.

Geminoid F's smile may have been particularly reassuring because my unappealing mug was right next to it. But why would the reporters smile at an android? Well, when someone smiles at you, it's only natural to smile back. Even so, some reporters looked embarrassed by their own reaction. Watching them, I became convinced they could easily fall in love with Geminoid F. I pressed some of those embarrassed reporters to ask her more questions, asking whether there wasn't something else they would like to know, but this seemed to make them all the more embarrassed. The whole situation was quite amusing, but also highly intriguing; it showed me just how important a smile can be when trying to make a robot seem humanlike.

Research has shown that emotions are the most rapid form of communication. When we see a happy or an angry face, we learn something of the person's emotional state without a word being spoken. I hadn't made sufficient allowance for such means of communication when I built Geminoid HI-1. I look angry by default, and if asked what other emotions my face can express, I'm not sure I could give a good answer. Because I always look angry, I had always assumed that emotions are subjective, dependent on how the receiver interprets them. However, objective emotional expressions also exist. My expression is likely one example. Geminoid F's smiling face is another; everyone interprets it as a smile, so we might call it an "objective smile." Such objective emotional expressions that are interpreted the same way by most people are an important means of communication, especially when interacting with strangers. At a minimum, they will be necessary to make androids seem more human.

Little past research into robots that interact with humans, or systems for conversing with humans, has explicitly dealt with emotion. Of course, many toy-like robots can look happy or angry, but emotion has rarely been considered in the development of robots or systems that perform services in place of people. This may be due to a preconception that robots that accurately respond to commands with no emotion involved are more useful.

Recently, however, research incorporating emotional expressions has begun. For example, Clifford Nass at Stanford University is researching how spoken guidance in car navigation systems affects drivers. He has found that male and female voices, as well as the manner in which they speak, alters drivers' behaviors.

Skillful incorporation of not just verbal accuracy but also emotional expressions facilitates conversation. In cases where the textual content of a dialogue is unclear, emotional expressions can help us interpret the intended meaning of vague statements. For example, the word "hate" can mean many things in different contexts; it's how that word is said that allows us to interpret the speaker's true meaning. In terms of conveying information, therefore, the emotional context of a statement is sometimes more important than the words actually spoken.

Robots and systems that convey information only through words will unfailingly give a mechanical impression. A good example is the automated voice systems you're greeted with when calling a company for technical support. These systems generally ask you to press a button according to what you need, then redirect you to another automated response. There is no question as to whether you're dealing with a machine. After being asked to make selection after selection, the whole thing starts to feel like more trouble than it's worth, to the point where I often just hang up. But I wonder if my response would be different if automated systems used more emotional expressions. Perhaps if users felt a bit more humanity in these systems, they would be more willing to put up with the hassle and use them as intended.

Humans are well equipped for dealing with other humans. Emotions are a big part of that ability, and cannot be ignored. If emotional expressions can be incorporated in a way that promotes user adaption to systems and allows information to be more accurately communicated, they should be extensively used, whether in an automated telephone system or a robot that converses with humans.

Are such emotional expressions a human-specific phenomenon? A zoologist might claim that higher-order animals like monkeys and chimpanzees experience emotions as well. Even dogs and other animals we live in close proximity to seem to experience joy, sadness, and other humanlike emotions. In fact, emotions in a broad sense seem to be fundamentally characteristic of many animals.

Let's consider this further. In particular, why do animals require emotional expressions in the first place? To aid communication between individuals, of course, but couldn't that be done without emotion? Perhaps this is one way to preserve individuals and species. Specifically, I believe that the purpose of emotional expressions is the exchange of information for purposes such as finding food or mates.

Beyond research of emotional expression lies research into sexuality. Interestingly, the study of animal communication and sociality always leads to debate of issues related to mating and other aspects of sexuality. Fireflies shine their pretty lights in search of a mate. Group societies of primates such as chimpanzees and bonobos are observed and described in terms of communication originating from sexual desire. However, studies of human society and interpersonal communication tend to separate issues of sexuality from those related to superficial communication. While everyone agrees that emotional expressions are important, there has been little deep research into their origins.

This is not to say that there has been no such research. My point is that there has been little opportunity for discussing issues related to sexuality and communication together. Indeed, sexuality is most commonly discussed from a medical perspective, and only rarely alongside debate regarding the general development of human society or interpersonal communications.

Given the extremely complex nature of humanity, I suppose it is difficult to have simple discussions of sexual issues. People also likely hesitate to pursue such lines of inquiry from a naïve assumption that they will lead to sexual discrimination. In the future, however, I think more research needs to be conducted between communication and sexuality so we can consider more essential aspects of communication, such as its origins. In a nutshell, it is sexual desire that draws together men and women, both directly and indirectly.

Touching Geminoid F

What does it feel like to speak with a Geminoid? Apparently, many people enjoy it more than speaking with another human.

Geminoids are of course androids, and clearly not human. Even so, almost no one considers Geminoid F and its model to be completely separate individuals. If nothing else, they look far more similar than any two people should. So what's different about them? I'm still not entirely sure, even five years after developing my first Geminoid, but I have noticed several interesting phenomena.

Allow me to start by relating the experiences and thoughts of one of the researchers who assisted me as a programmer when developing Geminoid F, a man for whom I will use the pseudonym "Dr. Ozaki." He told me that at first, he was very hesitant about touching it. It looked so life-like, he said, that touching its body was too much like touching the body of a real woman. Nevertheless, our research required he do so. Dr. Ozaki finally managed to pull this off without hesitation about a week after Geminoid F arrived at our lab. When an opportunity later arose for him to meet the android's model, however, he said it was extremely embarrassing.

From Dr. Ozaki's perspective, it was as if this body that he had been freely touching in the lab was standing before him, alive. What had previously been an android, devoid of consciousness, was now an actual person, talking to him no less. For some reason he couldn't quite put his finger on, this was very disturbing.

I wonder what might cause such feelings. Was he guilty over having touched her unconscious body? Of course, he was well aware that the android and its model are completely separate entities, and that the android does not have a consciousness. Even so, the similarity in appearance was apparently enough to cause an instinctual feeling of guilt.

This demonstrates the importance of appearance in recognizing people. Returning to the question of what aspects of a person we consider when determining their identity, appearance comes first. However, observations of humans reveal many unique characteristics other than appearance, such as their smell, their voice, the things they talk about, and the gestures they make. Might any of these prove useful in identifying individuals?

To investigate this, I used a Geminoid to conduct what I call a "doppelgänger experiment." I'll admit that I have not yet obtained any clear-cut results, but it is an intriguing experiment, and therefore, I believe, worth describing. The goal of this experiment was to determine whether individual characteristics are present in speech, and the extent to which we can identify people through speech patterns alone (as opposed to vocal characteristics). Geminoids make this experiment possible, because they allow us to speak with different people through a body with a single appearance and voice.

However, we couldn't simply have various people operate the Geminoid. Geminoids replay their operators' voices as-is, so they sound different depending on who operates them. We therefore arranged to always have the same person operating the android, while another person stood behind them. When the standing person said something, the operator repeated what was said so that it was replayed through the Geminoid. This meant the Geminoid always spoke with the same voice.

No doubt you are wondering if this setup would really work, but people are better at impersonations than you might think. It is particularly easy to exactly mimic something you've heard only moments ago. This is easy enough to verify for yourself, and I urge any doubters to try it.

We had various people speak via Geminoid and its operator in this way, and asked those conversing with the Geminoid whether they could figure out who they were speaking with. The results were quite interesting: subjects were only able to determine whether or not they knew the person. In other words, speech mannerisms alone were not enough to identify someone, but they were enough to determine whether they were speaking with a stranger.

I suppose this means that compared to the way we look, the way we speak doesn't distinguish us much. This offers further evidence of the extent to which we use appearance to identify people.

I've described how Geminoid F's appearance as an attractive woman made my colleague uncomfortable upon meeting its model, but what about Geminoid HI-1? In that case, I was there before the android was developed and delivered to our laboratory, so apparently he didn't feel strange interacting with me after its arrival. Unfortunately, direct comparisons with the case of Geminoid F are not possible. There were several interesting related episodes, however.

As with Geminoid F, the development of Geminoid HI-1 started with programming its motions. Unlike F, however, HI-1 had fifty actuators, so its programming took quite a long time. In particular, the programmer spent over a month recreating my idiosyncrasies in detail. At first, we used a student programmer, but he soon complained that he'd started having dreams about me every night. We therefore reassigned programming duties to a psychology researcher from the UK, on the assumption that he would feel less pressure than one of my students. That was indeed the case, and he completed the program without issue.

In another episode, soon after Geminoid HI-1 was complete, a television crew came to report on it at the ATR Intelligent Robotics and Communications Laboratories. They covered us over two days, during the first of which I answered their questions while operating the Geminoid from Osaka University. On the second day I visited ATR to talk directly with the reporter whom I'd been speaking with through Geminoid HI-1.

The main topic of our conversation was how little human beings know about themselves. I described in detail how using a Geminoid had taught me that in some ways, other people know me better than I know myself. The reflections I see in mirrors every day are reversed, so the face that I know is slightly different from the one everyone else sees. Further, I realized that others were highly conscious of mannerisms that I had never noticed in myself. The reporter told me she had never thought about such things, and as a result of our conversation had spent a sleepless night wondering how little of herself she actually knew.

Even more interesting, the reporter said she found my Geminoid less intimidating than my actual self. I already knew that my expressions and speech tend to make students nervous, but apparently this was also the case for someone I'd just met. Importantly, however, my Geminoid softened these rough edges, putting the reporter somewhat more at ease when interacting with me. I realized that during meetings with staff and students as well, my students spoke up more when I attended via Geminoid than when I was there in person.

Lowered mental barriers

Students speaking with Geminoid HI-1 of course know that it is an android. They can touch it freely, and should they need to get away from it, the immobile HI-1 wouldn't be able to pursue them. Not that they attempt to do such things while I am speaking to them through the android, but they interact with it differently than they do with my non-Geminoid self. Somewhere in the back of their minds they remain conscious that they are dealing with an object. A Geminoid just doesn't have the same physical presence as a human body.

I believe this is akin to our relationship with people we are close to. When we speak with someone we don't know well, we maintain a certain mental and physical distance. The better we know someone, the narrower this distance. A kind of mental barrier enforces the social rules regarding familiarity as a criterion for how we interact with other people. When Geminoids are viewed as objects, these mental barriers are lowered from the beginning. I imagine that this is one reason why many people find it easier to speak with Geminoid HI-1 than with me.

This phenomenon was even more evident with Geminoid F. Before our media event, Dr. Ozaki spent several hours with Geminoid F while its model practiced using the android from another location. Several people had operated Geminoid F in the past, but as I have mentioned before its model was by far the most skilled. When they were done I asked how it went, and he replied, blushing furiously, "Being with her is … a lot of fun."

Dr. Ozaki had of course met Geminoid F's model before, and had even spent a significant amount of time with her. However, he said he felt a much stronger attraction to the Geminoid F as operated by its model than to the model herself. He seemed to have even developed something of a crush on it. Reflecting on why this might be the case, I concluded that this, too, must be the result of lowered mental barriers. Geminoid F is an android, so there are no laws or norms that prohibit touching its body; doing so is in fact an unavoidable part of our research. However, its appearance and manner of speaking are very humanlike, especially when a skilled operator is behind the controls. But despite the model's very convincing performance, Dr. Ozaki recognized Geminoid F as an entity for which requirements for physical and emotional distance were removed. I imagine the experience was similar to being with someone he was in a very close relationship with, like a girlfriend.

Something very interesting also happened immediately after the media event. When it was over, many of those in attendance wanted to have their photographs taken with Geminoid F, so we asked them to line up and take turns. One person posing for a photo, a man of some advanced age, took the liberty of holding F's hand, angering Dr. Ozaki. I certainly understood his reaction. Geminoid F may be "just" an android, but even so it is a very humanlike one, and furthermore at that moment it was being operated by its model. It seemed only polite to ask permission before holding its hand, so it felt as if this man was taking liberties on the assumption that he could treat an android any way he wished. And he wasn't the only one.

I asked the model what she thought about this. She replied that while she wasn't happy about it, it didn't bother her too much. She didn't sound very convincing, though, and none of us were particularly comfortable with such displays of the male psyche. In future photo sessions we asked participants not to touch the robot, saying that doing so would degrade its skin.

So far as its model was concerned, however, these encounters with strangers were not all bad. She told me that she was normally shy and found it difficult to talk with strangers, but not when speaking through the Geminoid.

One of the main reasons for this was that since most people coming to see Geminoid F were very interested in androids, they were highly motivated to engage with it. When Geminoid F smiled at them, they were the ones who became embarrassed, so she didn't need to feel nervous when speaking with them. She also said that she wasn't as shy when meeting someone in person after having spoken to them through Geminoid F; they had already broken the ice, so her shyness was alleviated. I find it highly interesting that remote control of an android can result in such a significant change in psychological state with regard to others.

I also asked the model what it felt like to use Geminoid F to talk with someone she was already close with. For instance, Dr. Ozaki had been working with Geminoid F since just after its development and was very attentive to it. When the press was coming, for example, he was always careful to ensure that its hair and clothing were arranged just so. I noticed that after fixing its hair, he would give it a little pat on the head, in a kind of "now you're all set, good luck" gesture.

I asked the model what she thought about these little pats when they occurred while she was operating the Geminoid, and she said they made her very happy. In other situations too, such light displays of affection through a Geminoid resulted in a sense of familiarity, she said. When I asked her how she would feel if Dr. Ozaki directly touched her head in person—something he of course had never done—she said that would certainly be embarrassing. It is clear from these examples that Geminoids present new forms of human interaction.

What about love?

Perhaps the discussion above has caused some readers to wonder whether it is truly possible to feel attracted to a Geminoid. Or does the fact that Geminoid is an android make romantic attraction even easier?

As described earlier, in the fall of 2009 we took Geminoid HI-1 to Linz, Austria and set it up in one corner of an ordinary café for three weeks. During that time, I performed an experiment in which I operated HI-1 to interact with local residents there. One of the questions I asked women was, "Do you think you could fall in love with this Geminoid?" Interestingly, most answered "yes." This wouldn't have been so surprising had they been speaking to a human, but I imagine they must have answered the way they did with regards to the Geminoid for a different reason.

Geminoid HI-1 is a very well-made android, but upon close inspection it is clearly not human—its hands are a little too large, for example, and the skin around its neck looks slightly unnatural. Most importantly, its motions—especially larger ones—are somewhat awkward due to the difficulty of making it move exactly like a human. In fact, I believe most women were able to admit they could fall in love with HI-1 specifically because it is an android. As described above, our mental barriers tend to be lowered when we're interacting with an android, which makes them highly approachable even on a first encounter.

I have made several attempts to determine whether feelings of familiarity toward a Geminoid transfer to its operator. Some fellow researchers once came to see Geminoid F after its completion, and I asked its model to operate it during their first meeting. After they had spoken for a while and the researchers had seen F's smiles and frowns and such, I brought the model in to join the meeting. Nearly all the researchers said meeting her in person was very embarrassing.

They explained that they had been at ease when speaking to the android, and even felt comfortable touching its body. When presented with a nearly identical human, however, they felt as if they had been doing something inappropriate. I don't experience this myself—probably because I am so used to working with androids, and simply view them as research subjects—but the same thing happens every time I try it with other visitors; they have no problem becoming familiar with the Geminoid, but when its model enters the room, their mental barriers go back up and they experience feelings of guilt.

One might therefore consider time spent conversing with Geminoid F as wasted in terms of becoming acquainted with its model, but that's not the case. If nothing else, when the model stops operating the Geminoid and enters the room, she does not feel as if this is her first meeting with the visitors. Since a degree of familiarity was attained through their earlier conversation via android, her mental barriers are far lower than they would have been upon a true first encounter.

I previously mentioned that while the model is shy, using Geminoid F allows her to talk to strangers with relative ease. The android is thus very useful because it allows her to be bolder than normal, reducing the distance between herself and others. In contrast, visitors become somewhat nervous when presented with the model after having talked with her Geminoid, so from their perspective the distance between themselves and the model has temporarily increased. Use of the Geminoid thus results in a significant change in the psychological states of both its operator and those speaking with it.

CHAPTER

ANOTHER YOU

Geminoid as a sounding board

Humans are unable to accurately hear the sound of their own voice. You've probably had the experience of hearing a recording of your voice and being surprised at how different it sounds from what you're used to. As this experience demonstrates, the voice we hear when we speak is very different from what others hear. We can make use of this phenomenon in that so long as a Geminoid sufficiently mimics your speech patterns, it can sound like you, regardless of whose voice it speaks with—that is, regardless of who operates it. Major characteristics such as gender must be kept the same, of course, but there's a lot of leeway in whose voice is used.

I'd like to try using this feature of Geminoid HI-1 to converse with myself. When faced with a difficult decision, perhaps you've had the experience of having a two-sided conversation in your head—something like the back-and-forth between a devil and an angel on someone's shoulders in cartoons, one trying to convince them to do something bad, the other to remain good. This ability to split our consciousness in two to argue both sides of a dilemma is an important part of how our personalities form and how we make decisions about the direction our lives will take. What I want to know is how it would feel if one of those two aspects of myself were personified.

As I've discussed, we don't know ourselves as well as we think we do. The fact that we sometimes experience regret or pause to reflect on the consequences of what we've done indicates that we do not always live up to our own expectations. But I believe that it is through repeated regret and reflection that we gradual-

I want to be able to speak to myself. (HI-1 is on the right)

ly come to know ourselves and form our personalities. By bringing Geminoid into this process of character formation, I suspect we might be able to better make realistic decisions.

A person limited to the confines of their own mind sometimes makes character-shaping decisions based on convenience. In particular, someone placed in an immoral position may avoid taking an objective view of their immoral act. This might not be quite so easy if the "devil on their shoulder" took on a physical form like Geminoid. If they were faced with a self that promoted immoral acts—an embodiment of what they would become after deciding to act that way—would they still make that decision? Or imagine creating a self that is always too honest to make any money, but is constantly jealous of those who do. As these examples suggest, I imagine that bringing physical simulations of ourselves into the real world will be very useful in promoting self-awareness and character formation.

I wish I could give you the details of how creating my Geminoid affected me, but unfortunately, the truth is I'm still not sure. My research has gained some fame, the effects of which are so large it is difficult to separate notoriety from any specific effects that Geminoid itself may have had on me.

I will discuss this in more detail later, but very briefly, I have come to feel a great deal of pressure to keep my appearance the same as my Geminoid's. Geminoids don't gain weight, nor do they age, so I feel like I'm not allowed to, either. I suppose this is the one clear influence Geminoid has had on me.

A convincing conversation partner

I suspect that Geminoid F had an even stronger effect on its model than HI-1 had on me. As I described before, she viewed her android as a kind of improved version of herself. It had nicer skin, better posture, and always maintained a dignified composure. I suppose that in a sense, the android seemed to be maintaining a kind of ideal emotional state. When presented with such an ideal version of yourself, it's hard not to make comparisons.

Depending on how well the android is constructed, of course, you might feel the opposite—that it is an example of something you definitely do not want to become. A skillfully made android, however, will have unblemished silicone skin never seen in any human and perfect posture as dictated by an aluminum framework that will never slouch. An android is furthermore always calm and collected. For some, this android-like state represents an ideal.

Ultimately, I would like to conduct an experiment in which Geminoid F attempts to convince its model of various things. The model once said, "If Geminoid F tried to convince me of something, I'd probably listen to what it had to say." No doubt, the words of an ideal self would carry weight. If the Geminoid F gave its model advice—even advice that she had received from others and ignored—she might find herself paying attention and finding ways to improve herself. I'm still trying to determine through trial-and-error the best way to conduct this experiment. As one example of what we might try, the F model mentioned that she has long wanted to study English but never manages to keep at it. But what if Geminoid F could teach her? Might that make a difference?

The problem with this example is that learning English takes too long. As an alternative, I wonder if Geminoid F might serve as an effective conversation partner when its model needs to talk through a problem. A professional counselor could remotely operate the android, but the model would be interacting with Geminoid F, which might have a bigger impact since she

Geminoid F speaking with its model.

would feel like she was receiving counseling from herself. The model might experience the illusion of solving and recovering from problems on her own. If that is the case, Geminoids have the potential to play a very important role in counseling.

In a somewhat related experiment, the current Geminoid is playing the role of observer in outpatient departments at Osaka University Hospital and the University of Tokyo Hospital. During outpatient visits, patients are normally seen by a single doctor. This puts the patient in a vulnerable position, which can often be intimidating.

Geminoid F in an actual medical care facility.

We introduced androids into that scenario. Specifically, the android sits next to the doctor, facing the patient. Image processing technologies detect the patient's expressions and nods of their head, allowing the android to nod along, smile, frown, and otherwise make empathetic gestures and expressions. Our experiments so far have shown that this puts patients at ease, allowing them to better understand what the doctor is saying.

Japan is currently facing a nursing shortage, making it difficult for nurses to find the time to accompany doctors during examinations that do not absolutely require their assistance. I hope androids might eventually help out in these situations.

More human than humans?

I sometimes feel that Geminoids are not just similar to their models but actually are more human than we are.

One reason is the expressiveness of their faces. When Geminoids are not being operated they are expressionless, but in the case of both my Geminoid and myself, many people interpret our expressionless faces as showing anger. This suggests that the emotional state of the viewer deter-

A vivid representation of death.

mines how an expressionless face is interpreted. An even better example is Geminoid F. Even minor changes to its expressionless face—slightly altering the angle from which it is photographed or subtly adjusting how wide it opens its eyes, for instance—can produce a wide variety of emotions. Indeed, I feel as if Geminoid F is capable of even more varied expressions than a normal person. Further, since Geminoid F is a robot, additional mechanisms for moving its face can be added as necessary. Geminoids and other androids thus present the potential for producing a far broader range of expressions than do normal humans.

There is one other aspect of expression in which I believe androids are superior to humans: their representation of death. My android, Geminoid HI-1, moves via fifty pneumatic actuators. When the air supply to those actuators is suddenly cut off, the air contained within them slowly leaks out, causing HI-1 to softly lose power throughout its body, finally slumping back into its chair, its head lolled back and its mouth and eyes open. Almost everyone who has seen this says it's like watching someone die. In that instant they completely forget that Geminoid HI-1 is an android, instead becoming convinced that they are observing a human death. I sometimes wonder whether humans are capable of such a vivid death scene.

In the next chapter, I will describe other ways in which these androids might someday outdo humans.

CHAPTER

8

ANDROIDS EXCEEDING HUMANS

The origins of android theater

Soon after developing Geminoid F, I had the idea of using it in something I call "android theater." I wanted to combine a beautiful visuals richness of artistic expression, and compelling narrative to present the viewing public with a certain vision of the "ultimate human."

I had previously worked with Kuroki Kazunari, chair of the robotics company Eager Co., Ltd., and the theater director Hirata Oriza in developing artistic content for what we called "robot theater," in which daily-life robots appear on stage alongside human performers. I had teamed up with Kuroki wanting to create some form of robotic theater, and at just around that time, Hirata approached me at Osaka University expressing a similar interest. The three of us ended up putting together two robot-theater productions written and performed by Hirata: *I, Worker* and *In the Heart of a Forest*.

After completing Geminoid F, I was convinced it would be an interesting addition to robotic theater and was eager to start. I told Hirata about my ideas for this "android theater," and he enthusiastically agreed to work on the project. Further, he immediately understood what I was after. At the time, he was in the middle of rehearsals for *In the Heart of a Forest*, so I was surprised he had time for anything else. Somehow, however, he managed to whip out a script for a twenty-minute performance, all while producing our other play.

Faced with the dilemma of how to use an immobile, seated android in a theatrical setting, he quickly came up with the idea of having it read

A scene from the robot theater production *I, Worker.*

poetry. I still remember him coming to see me after completing the first five minutes of the script to give me a preview with an actor operating Geminoid F. "What do you think?" he asked. I was amazed. The performance was exactly what

I'd hoped for in android theater. I can't take credit for the idea of having the android read poetry; I just sensed intuitively that there must be something interesting it could do. What I saw embodied that intuition.

A scene from the robot theater production *In the Heart of a Forest*.

Hirata is fond of saying, "I don't know *why* it's the right thing to do, just that it is." I suppose that's the nature of artistic talent, but it surprises me nonetheless. I had hoped to become a painter for a time when I was a student, so I'm not completely oblivious to the artistic mindset, but working with a professional like Hirata makes me all too aware of the talents I lack.

I suppose the role we engineers and scientists play is to back up the ideas of artists and performers with reasons. In the case of both robot theater and android theater, our job therefore comes after the show is over. Even so, after seeing those first five minutes of Hirata's in-progress android play, I became much more interested in it than in the second robot-theater production, and did my best to find holes in my schedule to attend every rehearsal I could.

An elusive ephemerality

I did my best to provide a few ideas for android theater. I was of course concerned with remote operation of the android, but I was also very particular about how the android was illuminated. I'm sure Hirata would have been equally concerned without my input, but I tried adjusting the lighting myself and was fascinated by how even minor changes could transform the viewer's impression of the android. Through experimentation, I came across a lighting scheme that seemed optimal for our android theater.

Specifically, we used a slightly yellowish bulb to spotlight the android

Geminoid F reciting a poem onstage. (Photo courtesy of Shinchosha Photography Department)

against a pitch-black background. Doing so made it look much more human. Watching the android read poetry under this lighting is truly exciting, like observing something just out of reach. I was powerfully drawn into the reading and wanted to keep listening on and on. It was a truly fascinating sensation, and I wasn't the only one who thought so; nearly everyone from my lab who saw the show reported the same feeling.

Here is a rough description of the show. We hear a voice slowly reciting Tanikawa Shuntaro's poem, *Sayonara*, on a dark stage. A spotlight on the android gradually brightens as the poem progresses, finally bringing the full stage dimly into view.

> *It's time for me to go now.*
> *I must leave right away.*
> *I'm not sure where I'm headed, but*
> *I'll be passing beneath a row of cherry trees and*
> *I'll cross at the light when I reach the boulevard.*
> *I have to go alone,*
> *using familiar mountains as a guide.*
> *I have to go alone,*
> *though I'm not sure why.*

At this point, the android looks very human, yet it emanates an almost divine aura unlike that of any human. The poem continues:

> *Forgive me, Mother.*

Treat Father well.
I'll eat all my dinner with no complaints.
I'll read books, more than I do now.
At night I'll look at the stars, and
during the day I'll talk to lots of people.
I'll find the thing that I love most and
take good care of it and live until I die.
So I'll be far away, but I won't be lonely.
It's time for me to go now.

The stage is now brighter, and we see the android, a dying young woman reclining in a chair in front of it. The woman says to the android, "I don't know why they bought you for me. I still don't know."

The android replies, "I'm sorry I couldn't be of more assistance."

The woman slowly stands, approaches the android, and places its hand against her cheek. "Another poem," she begs. The android recites a poem by Rimbaud, then two *tanka* poems by Wakayama Bokusui:

Let's leave, off for
mountains we have never seen.
Can you bear this loneliness?
How many mountains and rivers must I traverse
to find escape from solitude?
Today too, I journey on.

The young woman asks, "How many of you are there in the world?"

The android answers, "Around 200,000, I think, but some of us were destroyed. You can destroy me if that would make you feel

Acting with a human actress. (Photo courtesy of Shinchosha Photography Department)

better, if I could be of service in that way." Such statements give the android a sense of pathos and depth.

"I wonder if that would make me feel better?" the woman asks.

"I understand that most people feel regret after doing so," the android says. Hearing that answer somehow set my mind at ease because it suggested that in this world, at least, people valued androids.

The woman next recites a German poem by Carl Busse, which the android translates into Japanese for the audience:

> *Over the mountains, far to travel,*
> *people say, Happiness dwells.*
> *Alas, and I went in the crowd of the others,*
> *and returned with a tear-stained face.*
> *Over the mountains, far to travel,*
> *people say, Happiness dwells.*

Reflecting on this poem, the android says, "So the Japanese search for a land free of loneliness, while the Germans search for a land in which happiness dwells."

The woman replies, "Which will you give me? Happiness, or freedom from loneliness?"

"An android sees no difference," it says. "Would freedom from loneliness not itself be happiness?"

"Father bought you when he learned I won't be getting better. Isn't that horrible?"

"You wanted a robot that's more useful?"

Finally, the woman says, "I don't think I'll destroy you," then falls asleep. As she does, the android recites to her another poem by Tanikawa, *Far Away*:

> *I think I've gone farther than Yocchan.*
> *Farther than Tadashi.*

Farther than Goro and farther than Mom.
Maybe even farther than Dad, and his grandfather.
Goro left home on a Wednesday,
came back late Sunday night.
He came back thin, and muddy, and
with a thirst he could not slake.
Nobody knew where he'd been.
If I just kept walking and walking,
I wonder where I'd end up?
Would I someday find myself an old woman,
drinking my tea and remembering nothing of the day?
I hope I'd end up someplace even farther on than here,
some place where there's at least one person I love,
even if they've already passed on.
I hope there's at least one unforgettable memory there.
A place where the scent of the ocean comes wafting in from
      somewhere.
But I think I can make it much farther than the sea.

As the android recites this last poem, it almost seems filled with a humanlike sadness, to the extent where many people involved in the show were brought to tears.

I was particularly surprised to find that although this android performance was only twenty minutes long, each scene blended smoothly into the next as if by calculation, skillfully extracting a sense of humanness from the android. I suspect that Hirata may have set aside his work with robot theater to focus fully on android theater instead. In any event, his skill was clearly evident.

Perhaps the android evoked the ephemerality of life so vividly specifically because it is not human. I suspect that a human playing the same role would not be able evoke quite the same feelings and thoughts in the audience.

From the right, Hirata Oriza, the author, and Geminoid F.
(Photo courtesy of Shinchosha Photography Department)

While producing the piece with Hirata, I focused in particular on the android's humanness. To that end, I gave its operator very detailed instructions on how to control it. Later, however, Hirata suggested that we should retain some sense of it being a robot. In the performance, therefore, the android did not move as naturally as it was capable of. I suppose Hirata was concerned that presenting it in too humanlike a form would make it indistinguishable from a human actress. The result, however, was a performance better than what a human actor would have been capable of. That's what I think, anyway.

"No human is that pretty"

Further proof that androids have already exceeded humans in some respects was revealed in audience surveys conducted after each android theater production, of which there were four or five in 2010 in Nagoya and Tokyo. These surveys revealed some very interesting audience reactions, in particular regarding impressions of the android's poetry readings. Most viewers interpreted those poems as a message not from the poet but from the android. I felt exactly the same at certain moments.

Considering this, I asked both the android's model and the actress who operated it during the performance whether they could have done a better job of reciting the poems on stage than the android did. Both answered no, though neither could quite put into words why that was the case. I have a good idea, though—it's because in this case the android was superior to the human.

The audience survey also contained several other questions. For example, ninety percent of viewers said they found the android attractive, while only sixty percent said they found it humanlike.

I wonder what lies behind that thirty-percent difference. Could it be that androids have become so attractive they no longer seem humanlike? That's what I think. Audience members also made comments like "The android was so beautiful," "It had such glowing skin," and "No human is that pretty."

Beauty is not humanlike

Geminoids are modeled on specific humans, but unlike humans, their appearance does not change significantly from day to day based on how they feel. Their silicone skin is likewise unchanging, so it remains forever beautiful. They're always capable of the same smile or frown, and they can make these expressions on stage with perfect timing to show happiness or displeasure as the script demands. Further, their lines are written by Hirata Oriza, include poems by Tanikawa Shuntaro and others, and are delivered via remote control by a professional performer, making for a wonderful performance. The whole package is enough to erase any scent of humanity. One audience member even said the android looked like the Virgin Mary. *Very interesting*, I thought. The robot may have a human form, but the words coming from its mouth and the attitude expressed through its body have a purity devoid of human baseness.

Everyone wants to be considered attractive so that they draw the attention of others. But I can't help wonder just how attractive people really want to be. If given the opportunity to become as beautiful as a movie star, how many would do so without hesitation? For both men and women, extreme physical attractiveness may be no more than an unrealistic ideal. In other words, the ideal human as conceived by other humans is possibly inhuman. In this way, we are always pursuing an unrealizable goal.

Do people really want to be beautiful?

That being said, advances in medical technology may one day make attaining ideal beauty quite possible. Already, anyone with the money to spare can undergo cosmetic surgery to change their face however they wish. Even as we age, surgery can allow us to maintain a youthful appearance for a very long time.

Cosmetic surgery is extremely popular in South Korea, but many Japanese would likely hesitate to go quite so far. However, South Korean singers and performers are now all the rage in Japan. As I will describe in the next chapter, I believe this will soon make plastic surgery much more socially acceptable in Japan, so that someday, the streets will be crowded with beautiful men and women. I hope that such improvements to surface beauty will help to polish inner beauty as well.

I believe such trends can only go so far, however. If everyone became equally beautiful, individual identities would wither. I fear a society like this could even whittle away at the life force of its individual members, decreasing the vitality of society overall. The world of surrogates I described in a previous chapter is an extreme example of that scenario. In that world, everyone spends their entire life appearing to the outside world as they did at their prime. If they aren't happy with that appearance, they can change their robot to look however they want.

If that world of surrogates does someday arrive, will we always adopt the most attractive appearance possible? If so, we will become less like humans and more like robots performing android theater. Might we be able to push beyond that and select somewhat imperfect yet more human appearances in order to remain more like ourselves? Conversely, might we learn that appearances have nothing to do with human identity and values? Although no answers to these questions exist, they nevertheless raise important issues about humanity.

You, standing right before your own eyes

When we put on an android theater performance at the Aichi Triennale, an international arts festival in Nagoya, I had the opportunity to speak with Geminoid F's model and the performer who operated it during the show. Something very interesting happened when we met.

I asked the operator how she felt upon meeting with the android's model, and she said, "It's like I'm standing right in front of me."

For about a month before the android performance was presented, the operator constantly watched the android through a monitor and practiced with it until it felt like its body was hers. It wasn't just Geminoid F, however; she felt like its model, too, was an extension of her own body. No doubt it was a very strange experience to see "her" body acting on its own. A month of using an android is enough to create a genuine sense that this machine is your body. The feeling is so strong that upon seeing the android's model moving about, as natural as that may be, it's almost as if "your" body has been possessed.

There is no reason to assume that this feeling will be limited to situations like the android theater project. Masked wrestlers often wear their masks even when they aren't in a wrestling match, so I suspect they might view their masked figure as their true selves. Women's makeup is a more familiar example. A woman who always wears makeup when going out might consider her made-up self to be more "herself" than her natural self.

As I've mentioned, the model for F is somewhat shy, even when meeting other women, but she said she was not nervous at all when meeting the android theater operator after the show. By thinking of her as the person inside Geminoid F, the model apparently felt she already knew the operator.

The model said she loved the performance. Seeing Geminoid F—an android she had operated for so long that it felt like an extension of her own body—playing its role so skillfully was a truly moving experience for her. I imagine that being presented with the performer who had played that role felt like meeting an old friend, resulting in a sense of familiarity rather than nervousness.

When a stranger controls you better than you do

In further discussions, the model said she was a little humiliated at having seen someone operate Geminoid F even better than she could. The model had operated her Geminoid several times since the media event, and had always been its most skilled operator. With android theater, however, we had a professional performer intensively practice using Geminoid F for a month, so she had become adapted to the android and far more skilled at its operation. From the model's perspective, it must have felt as if someone had taken her form.

One possible response to the question of who owns Geminoid F's appearance might be "whoever can use it best." I imagine many people would agree, but in the case of android theater, the fact that the most skilled operator was not the android's model complicated the situation. Two people considered the same form to be theirs, potentially posing the odd situation of a struggle for ownership of the android's identity.

An independent being on stage

Android theater revealed far more complex aspects of humanity than any previous research on remotely controlled androids had. In laboratory experiments, Geminoid's appearance and the personality of its human operator come together only during the brief times during which it is being operated. It becomes a fleeting, intermediate being that is neither its model nor its operator. However, the Geminoid in the context of android theater is a little different. While on stage, Geminoid is clearly an independent being. When provided with a well-written script, a Geminoid becomes a human living within the story. I'm sure even the model felt the same way while watching the performance.

I believe we become ourselves—that is, we come to behave in certain ways in certain situations—through the accumulation of many experiences. We develop individuality by playing the various roles we find ourselves in. In the same way, both the android theater audience and we developers can accept Geminoid as an individual with its own personality.

Further, the Geminoid can be freed from the actress that is operating it, potentially allowing it to become an independent actor on the stage.

Truth be told, android theater does not require a human operator. After a single controlled performance, it would be easy enough to use computers to record the actress's speech and the Geminoid's precise movements, then replay that data in any future performance.

I wonder how an actress would feel, knowing that she is no longer needed for her performance. Her actual form never appears on stage, just a Geminoid that is speaking in her voice. Further, the lowered mental barriers inherent to androids allows them to become immeasurably attractive to the audience. Perhaps the actress would feel that her voice had been stolen. But regardless of how the details settle, androids clearly represent an unprecedented means of theatrical expression, and have potential for greatly advancing the performing arts.

Even Hirata agrees that theater does not necessarily require human performers. Until now that's all we've had, but if androids prove able to deliver performances more skillfully than humans, shouldn't they be the ones on stage? If robots are able to represent hidden aspects of humanity in performances that humans themselves are incapable of, they would be the far better performers.

Similar to how preconceived notions of robotic appearances have limited study of issues related to the appearance of robots designed to interact with humans, I believe that in the realm of theater, preconceived notions still dictate that acting must be performed by humans. We may have reached a stage at which androids developed for the purpose of investigating humanity can now assume roles once considered suited only to humans. This could represent a major step forward not only for the world of theater, but also for the humans who enjoy those performances. Theater evolved through technology will likely provide us with opportunities to more deeply consider the true nature of human beings.

MAKING OURSELVES LIKE ANDROIDS

Changing androids, changing humans

My look-alike android Geminoid HI-1 was fabricated in 2005, so as of 2010 it had been in existence for five years. We had performed minor work on it during that time, but now it was time for more serious repairs. In particular, its eyes weren't moving right.

Previous androids were fabricated with pneumatic actuators in place of motors for improved durability, but for Geminoid HI-1 we used servomotors to produce more humanlike eye movements. However, constantly using a servomotor inside an android covered in a silicone skin appeared to create problems, and they had started to wear out. HI-1 was highly durable compared to general humanoid robots, but after five years its motors were starting to stick, calling for major repairs within its head.

Since we were going to be working on HI-1's head, we decided to make some repairs to its face as well. Although it still closely resembled me, I was starting to hear comments that it looked slightly different. There were several reasons for this. First, silicone skin degrades with time; oils in the silicone dissipate after a few years, causing it to lose its shine. This can be repaired by replacing the oils. A potentially bigger problem is that silicone slowly stretches under the constant pull of gravity. In that respect, it is similar to how the skin in human cheeks tends to droop with age.

However, this problem isn't necessarily insurmountable. The extent of the stretching in Geminoid HI-1 in particular was less than we had expected, leaving its appearance largely unchanged. When an android's skin starts to droop, the first changes appear around its eyes. Specifically, the cheeks pull down on the lower eyelids, giving it an almost zombie-like appearance in extreme cases. My eyes are very narrow, however, so this wasn't a big issue for HI-1.

In fact, I had changed more than the android had. It is very difficult for a human to retain exactly the same body shape for five years, and I had gained a little weight since its initial development. I blame Geminoid HI-1's fame, which garnered me invitations to many interviews and lectures, along with the dinners that usually accompanied them. My coworkers made comments about how I'd started looking heavier than my Geminoid. I shrugged it off at first, but the more I heard it the more it bothered me. With a fat me and a slimmer android standing side-by-side, the android is of course more attractive. It made me feel like a slob, and inferior to my android.

I therefore decided to lose some weight. I tend to be stubborn, so once I'm motivated enough to have made a decision, I see it through. However, this wasn't the first time I'd thought I should slim down. I'd even tried buying mail-order exercise equipment a few times, but never used those devices for more than a few days. I think my motivation at the time wasn't so much losing weight as seeing what it was like to use the equipment as a tool. Using those devices right after I'd bought them was therefore lots of fun, but less so once I'd gotten used to them, so they went unused after that. But now that I'd really set my mind on losing weight, my first concern was how best to do so without buying any exercise equipment.

The user's manual that comes with a piece of exercise equipment describes which muscles it is designed to work out. This made me wonder which muscles I should exercise to lose the most weight, namely, which muscles in the human body use the most energy when they're working. I believe that would be the abdominal muscles. Also, considering that the biggest difference between Geminoid HI-1 and myself at the time was the girth of our waists, I decided to work on my abs to reduce the size of my stomach.

The best way to exercise your abs is to do sit-ups, which require no exercise equipment. At first, I decided to do sit-ups in bed just before going to sleep. When I first started, I was only able to do around five or ten in a row. I was surprised to find that to be the extent of my abilities, but apparently having no way to hold your feet down makes sit-ups very difficult. I therefore went to a nearby store and spent five thousand yen on a bench designed for doing sit-ups. It was just a simple workout bench, but one end had an attachment for holding your feet. I started doing my sit-ups using this bench laid flat, and within a week I was able to do fifty, then one hundred sit-ups. This really pushed my stubbornness button, making me want to see just how far I could go. Next, I tried elevating one end of the bench so my feet were about fifty centimeters higher than my head. This forces you to lift more of your body weight, making sit-ups much more difficult. With the bench tilted like this, at first I could again only do around ten sit-ups, but I kept at it every night before going to bed. Again, the number of reps I could accomplish gradually increased until I could do one hundred in a row.

Sit-ups replace abdominal fat with muscle, making your stomach feel much tighter. This doesn't reduce body weight, though. Really slimming down requires a dietary overhaul. Asking myself how I might naturally improve my diet, I hit on the idea of doing a round of sit-ups any time I found myself wanting a nighttime snack.

If you really want to strengthen your abs through sit-ups, you have to do them until they hurt. As anyone who works out knows, muscle pain indicates damage to muscle fibers, which when repaired become tougher. A side-effect of pain in your abdominal muscles is that it eliminates hunger, so when you're hungry, doing sit-ups until it hurts helps cut back on between-meal snacks. I was soon losing weight so quickly I looked forward to getting on the scale every day.

After a while, however, I started getting stomach pains. These pains felt like the hunger pains I used to alleviate by eating. Sure enough, eating a light meal would make them go away, but this got in the way of losing weight. I therefore decided to consult with a doctor. The cause of my stomach pains was exactly what I'd suspected: the doctor said my bulked-up abdominal muscles were putting pressure on my stomach, causing pains like those caused by fasting. He told me taking an antacid for a week should take care of the problem, so I left with a prescription. Sure enough, a few days later I was pain-free.

About three months after I started doing sit-ups, my waist had shrunk by about ten centimeters and I had lost ten kilograms. Actually, I had achieved a better body than Geminoid HI-1.

My weight hasn't changed much since then. My body-fat percentage has fallen to around ten percent, so losing any more weight could conversely be bad for my health. I still do sit-ups, but now with the goal of maintaining my current weight and waist size. So far, I've been able to do so for about a year.

Thinner than Geminoid

I had become so focused on my diet, I forgot that my original goal was to match Geminoid's body. Instead, I went too far and became slimmer than Geminoid.

Honestly, though, it felt good. Everyone around me commented on how I now looked better than my Geminoid, which made me feel as if I had beaten it. Further, tightening up my abs and losing weight markedly improved my motor skills, making me feel physically younger. Even if it meant being thinner than Geminoid HI-1, I had no intention of gaining back any of the weight I'd lost.

Wanting to put my recovered motor skills to the test, I challenged some of our younger researchers to a physical fitness competition. This was around the time of the conference in Austria. Lunchtime came at a time when five or six of us were viewing exhibitions in a basement exhibit space, and we decided to eat at a café on the third floor. I proposed taking the stairs and seeing who reached the third floor first. Everyone other than me was in their thirties, and therefore probably figured they would never lose to me, so they quickly agreed to my challenge (admittedly, they may have just been hesitant to decline a proposal made by someone in a senior position). Anyway, I won the race. That is when I truly felt that through dieting I had regained something of my youth.

In a sense, then, I was younger than I'd been when I developed Geminoid HI-1. There was still one problem, though: my face, which now looked decidedly older. A little fat padding out the face makes us look younger. In my case, dieting had deepened the "marionette lines" running from my nose to the corners of my mouth, which made me look definitely older. Losing weight across your entire body means losing fat from your face, which increases wrinkles. I wish there were a diet that allowed slimming the body but not the face, but unfortunately no such thing exists.

Creating a copy of oneself provides powerful motivation for wishing to hold on to youth. But in a case like mine, where my duplicate will always be on display as a representation of my research, many people will compare me with my android and tell me what they think. Also, Geminoid HI-1 is a product of my research, so I can never throw it away, no matter how much I might want to; it is a version of myself that I must always face. I can neither dispose of nor ignore this past self. This naturally becomes a motivation to change so as to better match what once was.

When asked wherein lies my identity as a researcher, I point to Geminoid HI-1, a past self that in some ways looks better than I do now. Watching the distance between us increase is like watching myself be split in two. Geminoid HI-1 is the me that others recognize, but the more I age, the more I must point to Geminoid as what I once was. This is a very lonely feeling. If possible, I want to remain forever identical to Geminoid HI-1.

What to fix

Prior to repairing Geminoid HI-1's head, we had to make a decision: keep its appearance the same, or update it to look as I did now?

An argument could be made for updating it, but I didn't really want to make it look like my aged self. I suppose I didn't want to face how much I had aged; I would rather try to revert to what I had been five years before.

That's when I met Dr. Kinugasa of the Kinugasa Clinic, a well-known hospital for plastic surgery. We met by chance, through a common acquaintance. At first we were just drinking buddies, but when I mentioned this issue to him, he said the simple solution would be to update myself through plastic surgery.

I'm sure many people would hesitate at the idea of plastic surgery, but it is not as big a deal as it once was. Before undergoing my procedure, Dr. Kinugasa gave me a tour of his clinic's facilities and explained what he would do. The advanced state of laser therapy was particularly surprising to me. I had heard that lasers can easily erase moles, but I learned that there are many other kinds of lasers, too. For example, one type tightens subdermal cellular structures, thereby reducing wrinkles. I can't remember the exact number, but I think the Kinugasa Clinic had something like ten different kinds of lasers. Simple cosmetic procedures do not even require scalpels. Most, in fact, involve only lasers and injections. Many people have the impression that undergoing cosmetic surgery means having scalpels carve up their natural-born face, but that is no longer the case. Laser therapy is simpler than applying makeup and far more effective. Unfortunately, most of the lasers Dr. Kinugasa uses are not manufactured domestically, forcing him to import them himself based on his personal judgment regarding their efficacy and his sense of responsibility as a doctor. This makes these devices very expensive. Even so, I believe it won't be long before nearly everyone makes use of plastic surgery.

In the end, considering the high cost and labor involved in fixing a Geminoid, I realized it would be far quicker and cheaper to fix myself instead. Fabricating a new skin for my Geminoid's head would have cost around three million yen [approximately US$30,000]. Furthermore, creating the cast of my head needed to do so would require over half a day of my time, more than would be required for me to rejuvenate myself.

At first, Dr. Kinugasa proposed significant modifications to make me look identical to Geminoid HI-1, but that made me a little nervous. After all, I could perform minor changes to my Geminoid without too much money or effort, so why make myself look like an aging robot? I also didn't want it to be obvious that I had undergone plastic surgery. I spoke with Dr. Kinugasa again about how we could fix some obvious defects, like the drooping around my eyes and the lines down my nose and mouth. He told me simple fixes like that could be performed using only lasers and injections.

The first procedure I underwent was called "ThermaCool," a treatment that tightens subdermal structures to produce an effect similar to a facelift. The principal is similar to that behind a treatment used on stiff shoulders, in which a low-frequency electric current is passed between two electrodes attached to your body to cause the muscles to contract. ThermaCool uses a high-frequency current between an electrode placed on the face and another held in one hand. This stimulates subdermal skin to a certain depth. Dr. Kinugasa explained that the effects last for around six months.

The treatment itself was extremely simple. My face was covered with electrodes, each approximately two centimeters square, focusing on areas with particularly deep wrinkles. These were left on for around thirty minutes. I heard that some people find the procedure painful, but I felt no pain at all. The effect is not immediate; results are supposed to appear after two or three days. Sure enough, several days later my face looked clearly tighter, as if I had undergone a facelift.

I visited Kinugasa Clinic again a week later so that staff could verify the effects of the procedure and use hyaluronic acid injections along my facial folds to eliminate the deep wrinkles that ThermaCool couldn't completely remove. Getting facial injections sounds a little scary, but they were nearly painless. They first numbed my face with something like dry ice, then Dr. Kinugasa quickly administered a series of injections. I felt a little prick, far less painful than a shot in the arm. The whole thing was over in around fifteen minutes.

Hyaluronic acid injections immediately erase even deep wrinkles. There's a slightly unnatural puffiness on either side of the wrinkle at first, but that goes away after a few days. Hyaluronic acid gets absorbed into the body, so its effects don't last forever, but they don't completely disappear, either, since the acid activates subdermal tissues.

Moles and identity

Besides getting rid of some facial wrinkles, I also removed a mole below the corner of my left eye. "Let's get rid of it, it'll just take three minutes," Dr. Kinugasa said, but I thought the procedure over at length before deciding to go ahead with it, far more contemplation than I needed before deciding to get rid of my wrinkles.

Wrinkles appear and deepen with age, so I'd prefer to have none. After all, getting rid of wrinkles feels like regaining youth. But moles are different. My mole wasn't a sign of age, it was a personal characteristic that had been part of my face since I was a child. It wasn't particularly attractive, so if it had appeared later in life I'm sure I would have wanted to get rid of it. But it had become so familiar to me I hesitated to have it removed. I've heard that laser removal of moles has become very common, primarily among school-age girls wishing to remove any blemish from their face at an early stage. It's a lot harder to get rid of something you've lived with for forty years.

After a while, however, I began to consider myself strange for getting so hung up about a mole. I knew I would have removed it without hesitation if it wasn't for those forty years, but why, exactly? What difference did forty years make? As a researcher I was constantly pursuing new ideas, and my research was all about finding new identities. I hadn't thought I was one to cling to my past self, but this mole showed me that I did. As soon as I considered the situation in this way, I decided to get rid of the mole. It seemed a way to disassociate my current self from my past self.

As the doctor had promised, it was gone in just three minutes. The mole was quite large, some six or seven millimeters in diameter and two or three millimeters deep, but the doctor easily cut it away with a laser scalpel and used another laser to blast away the pigmentation.

When I mentioned to people that I'd had my mole removed, everyone's first response was, "What are you going to do about the mole on Geminoid HI-1?" But removing a mole from an android is even simpler than removing one from a human—just scrape it away with a knife and repaint.

The remarkable similarity between cosmetic surgery and android fabrication

After having cosmetic surgery, I realized how similar the technologies are to those used in android fabrication.

I once met a man who worked in Hollywood doing special-effects makeup. He had returned to Japan and was working with a cosmetic surgeon to develop an android-related business. Creating such a company is no easy task, but they were determined to apply SFX makeup techniques to cosmetic surgery, using androids to show how patients' faces would look after surgery.

Looking at the various pieces of equipment in Dr. Kinugasa's clinic, I saw devices that used lasers and others that used ultrasound. All were clearly medical devices, but while their purpose might be different, they resembled the equipment in an engineering laboratory, especially the laser-based machines. It struck me as odd that tools for treating humans and those for building machines could look so similar. Recently, even surgeons have begun using robots. One famous example is the Da Vinci Surgical System. A surgical theater using this system looks like a cleanroom for fabricating integrated circuits or pharmaceutical devices.

Setting aside the issue of whether technological advances have caused humans to be treated more like machines or machines more like humans, or a little of both, the end result is the same—humans and machines are becoming closer. When we fabricate androids in particular, we appear to be building people. We make a mold, use that to reproduce human skin in silicone, and apply makeup. Because we use various tools to put on the makeup, at this stage the android looks a lot like a patient undergoing cosmetic surgery using lasers. Of course, there are currently major differences between android fabrication and cosmetic surgery, even when the surgery uses lasers that look similar to those used in industrial applications. As android technology further advances and we use increasingly natural-looking materials for the skin, I suspect we will reach a point at which it is impossible for an outside observer to determine whether operations are being performed on an android or a human.

Unnoticed changes in appearances

Having regained a younger appearance so that I once again looked like Geminoid HI-1, I had recovered the identity my android had taken from me. However, I was sensitive to what others might think and how they might respond to what I'd done. Would they say, "As usual, I can't figure that guy out"? I actually enjoy being hard to figure out, so I wouldn't take that as an insult, but the possibility still bothered me.

Long story short, nobody even noticed. When I pointed at my face and asked people if they noticed anything different, several finally said maybe I looked a little younger, but no one I hadn't seen in a while noticed any difference. After a period of asking people I was close to if they noticed anything different, the whole thing started to feel silly. I had started out worried what people would say, but found myself disappointed to learn they were saying nothing at all. The only person who noticed anything was an NHK cameraman with whom I met frequently because he was working on a documentary about me. Possibly because he was so attuned to my appearance, he asked me if something had changed right after my surgery, without my even mentioning it.

Perhaps it was due to my dissatisfaction with this experience, but I started paying particular attention to my face in the mirror. In doing so, I noticed that faces change from moment to moment throughout the day. They get swollen when we don't get enough sleep, but mostly slim back down by noon. The way they firm up and wrinkle changes day by day, too. I had previously heard women complain about their skin being good one day and bad on others, but they always looked the same to me. Now I realized what they were talking about. People don't typically pay much attention to the average man's appearance, so should his face be a little smoother one day or wrinkled the next, few people would notice enough to mention that he looks different.

I had always assumed it was our face that most establishes identity, but as it turns out faces are in constant flux, the fine details at any point in time cannot be what we use to recognize people as themselves. Instead, recognition seems to be based on unchanging characteristics of faces. It therefore makes perfect sense that the appearance or disappearance of a few wrinkles doesn't matter much.

Then again, most of those who noticed something different about me when I asked them said I looked younger. Others said they knew something was different but only realized what it was when I told them. Age may thus be something we subconsciously feel more than consciously notice.

The link between physical and mental youth

With my body and face now both feeling younger, I had in a sense returned to what I was when I first developed Geminoid HI-1. This wasn't just a change in appearance; it also had a profound effect on my mental state.

When you become physically younger, you also become mentally younger. When your body feels old, you start to wonder how much time you have left. You sense your body's limits and become less adventurous than when you were younger. A younger face and body help you to forget your age, giving you a feeling of freedom. For a researcher like myself, this has a large effect on research themes and goals. In many cases, work done in a researcher's thirties gains some fame and comes to represent their research in general. Having gained some fundamental knowledge of the field, they are judged according to those first bold adventures in pursuing independent ideas. They later gain students who will continue their research, so it is no longer theirs alone—as leader of a research group, their work must foster the group's members. More important than taking on new challenges, therefore, is fleshing out the field of research they have already created. I had somewhat accustomed myself to that notion, but having regained a bit of my youth, I found myself wanting to do something big again.

A dash of audacity is crucial to technological development. So is the audacity to go beyond technical boundaries in pursuit of more artistic ideas. Science is an offspring of art. Art arises with no firm reasoning, but when we apply methodology and design to it, the result is technology. In technological development, too, true invention is the creation of something from nothing, and that requires an artistic sensibility. Therefore, engineers and researchers must first and foremost be artists, and remaining an artist requires the energy of youth. I had always wanted to gain an artistic sensibility and boldness, but a part of me hesitated to become an artist nonetheless. My returned youth helped to remove that hesitation.

The physical and mental aspects of regaining youth are deeply related. Like most people, I had always wanted to remain mentally young, but I considered this separate from feeling or appearing physically young. I'd assumed I could remain mentally young even as I became physically older. What I found, however, was that a truly youthful approach to work required that I also look and feel young. Physical youth goes a long way toward maintaining mental youth. Housing a young spirit in an old body takes considerable effort, but a young spirit can reside in a young body with ease.

"Antiaging" has become something of a buzzword in recent years, not just in products for women, but for men as well. Indeed, as our working lives lengthen, I believe both men and women will become increasingly concerned with antiaging products. Today it is mainly women who get cosmetic surgery, but as advancements in machines and information systems free more men from physical labor, they will become increasingly involved in work that demands interpersonal communication. We may thus see a boom in cosmetic surgery for men in just five or ten years.

The Geminoid F model wanted to be more like her android, which she considered her ideal. Seeing her Geminoid keep its young, attractive appearance, she said she wished she could do the same. To that end, she even cut her hair into a more youthful style. When I heard she'd done that, I worried she would look different from the android, but it wasn't a problem; we just gave Geminoid F the same new hairstyle. It took five years for me to start worrying about differences between my appearance and that of my android, but less than one year for her. It will be interesting to see how she continues to engage with her Geminoid in the future.

Age and identity

Speaking of both men and women being interested in antiaging makes me immediately think of movie stars. When we visualize famous movie stars, most of us think of them as they looked in their most famous film. For example, it is difficult to imagine Sylvester Stallone or Arnold Schwarzenegger in their current aged state. My hunch is that movie stars try to perpetually maintain their appearance from those most popular films as well, because I'm always surprised to hear how old they are.

I bring up the subject of movie stars because I suspect that we establish identities based on a specific age, namely the point we consider to be the peak of our lifetime. Once we pass that peak, we tend to imagine ourselves in social contexts as still having that past identity.

Movie stars leave behind indelible records of their past identities, in the form of films. Most people, however, have no such artifacts that retain their identity in such an extensive visual form. As we age, we may even gain new identities. Of course, movie stars can create more famous films as they age, thereby gaining new identities as well. However, given the tastes of the general public, a ninety-year-old movie star would have a hard time snagging a contract.

There are, however, cases such as that of Albert Einstein, where photographs taken at a later point in life become popularized and turn the person's appearance at that age into their public identity. While Einstein's true identity should lie in his formless theory of relatively, his physical appearance was largely unknown when he proposed that theory, which is likely why later photographs took precedence. Perhaps when people have a strong identity based on something other than appearance, society continues to update the appearance associated with their identity for as long as they are alive and functioning in the public sphere.

So where does that leave me? For better or for worse, the world knows me for my research on a copy of myself. While these are my research results, appearance plays a large role, so my identity has to some extent come to resemble that of a movie star. To free myself from the restrictions that imposes, I must allow my newly youthful self to once again head off on adventures, and thereby forge a new identity that has nothing to do with my appearance.

PORTABLE GEMINOIDS

The birth of Geminoid HI-4

As described in the previous chapter, I addressed the discrepancy between my own aging appearance and that of Geminoid HI-1 through dieting and cosmetic surgery, bringing us once again more or less into sync.

However, Geminoid HI-1 was fabricated to look like me when I weighed more, and the actual me was now thinner—and younger-looking—than it was. We tried modifying HI-1 to create Geminoid HI-2, which looked a little younger, but it still didn't look as young as I did. I therefore decided we had to create a new android from scratch that looked like the rejuvenated me.

I discussed this plan with a corporate engineer whom I'd been working with for many years, and we decided to use this as an opportunity for improving our fabrication techniques, using better materials to create an even more realistic Geminoid. The result was Geminoid HI-4.

I'll describe its primary features and our other reasons for developing it later in this chapter, but for now I'd like to focus on appearance. I repeatedly asked our laboratory staff and secretary to confirm that it looked exactly like me. To create an android that looks exactly like a specific human being, it is necessary to create a mold of that person, to make three-dimensional measurements using a scanner, and to meticulously reproduce the model's face. Because human skin is so pliable, however, it is also necessary to create a form in clay, a material that better lends itself to making minor adjustments. These adjustments to the clay model took significant effort.

We also wanted to make the android's hair more realistic. When fabricating the previous Geminoid, we had implanted hairs only along the hairline, covering the rest of its head with a wig, but with Geminoid HI-4 we decided to implant a full head of hair. I have particularly thick hair, so faithfully duplicating my head using only a wig was difficult. In fact, we ended up implanting around twice as many hairs as are used in a typical wig. The results were highly satisfactory; just as hair implants on a human look more natural than a wig, HI-4's head looked much more nat-

ural than previous models had, producing an effect that was extremely
similar to me.

You may have noticed the number-
ing gap, and indeed, we also built a
Geminoid HI-3. In that android, we
aimed for a fully electric power supply.
HI-4, F, and the other Geminoids used
pneumatic actuators as "muscles" for
moving their bodies, but in HI-3 we replaced these with direct-drive electric
actuators. These unfortunately had insufficient power for moving the an-

Geminoid HI-4, which is very similar to
how I look today.

droid in a humanlike way, but since then we have developed more
powerful electric actuators. In the future, we plan to develop a Geminoid
that does not require an air compressor for driving pneumatic actuators, allowing us to keep all its mechanisms contained within its body
and to provide power from batteries.

A simpler Geminoid with a focus on conversational abilities

One thing I learned through developing and testing various Geminoids is
that if the primary goal is conversing with humans, arm and leg movements are not particularly important. Much more important are facial
expressions and movements, along with the motions that accompany respiration, something we expect in any living human being. In other words,
creating a Geminoid that provides a satisfactory conversational experience requires movements of the back, neck and head in order to reproduce the subtle signals of life.

Limiting the number of moving parts in this way not only made the
Geminoid system much more compact, it also allowed us to break it down
and transport it easily. Further, the 200-volt compressor was no longer

needed to move the android's pneumatic actuators; a standard 100-volt power supply like those available in the average home was now adequate.

All this made the android much cheaper to build. The pneumatic actuators are the most expensive part of a Geminoid, to the point where overall development costs are largely a function of the number of actuators used. With Geminoid HI-4 we limited the number of actuators to sixteen, allowing us to fabricate its body for around ten million yen [around US$92,000].

A portable Geminoid as a self-substitute

Setting aside issues of appearance, my primary reason for creating this simplified Geminoid HI-4 was so that it could deliver lectures in my place. As I have described in previous chapters, Geminoids have high potential to act as substitutes for the person they are modeled after. However, Geminoid HI-1 had too many actuators, requiring a large support system that incurred some five million yen [around US$46,000] in airline shipping fees any time we wanted to send it to Europe. This of course prevented me from sending it out for lectures as often as I would have liked, and was the reason I wanted a more portable, simpler android. In fact, I already had a simpler android, namely Geminoid F, but I wanted to make HI-4 even easier to use and transport. Specifically, I designed the android so that its head can be removed at the neck, its upper and lower body can be separated at the waist, and its arms and legs can be removed.

When travelling by airplane, the upper and lower body parts can each be stored in the largest-model Rimowa aluminum suitcase, allowing us to check it as normal baggage. The head is of course small enough to fit in a suitcase, but is a very delicate piece of equipment that must be kept close at hand. We learned this lesson after it was completely broken from being shaken about on one journey; checked baggage can be treated very roughly in some countries. We considered wrapping it in multiple layers of impact-absorbent material before packing it, but even that was unlikely to prevent damage if the suitcase were roughly tossed about, so now we keep the head with us as carry-on luggage.

A Geminoid head is exactly the size of a human head, so it fits easily into a piece of carry-on luggage. The problem is that it contains many metal parts, and airport inspections of carry-on luggage are today very strict. Should an inspector decide that some part in Geminoid's head might be used as a blade, we would be forced to check the bag.

I well remember the first time I went through an airport security screening while carrying Geminoid HI-4's head. I was leaving on an international flight from a Japanese airport, and I figured that since Geminoids were well known in Japan, a brief explanation would be enough to get me through. Sure enough, the inspector at the security gate looked in my bag and asked me what I was carrying. I showed him photographs of the Geminoid and explained that this was its head, and he waved me through without issue. The problem came when I attempted to pass through security gates at overseas airports. I believe the first I passed through was in Frankfurt, where I had a connecting flight. I went through the gate first with my own bags, followed by an assistant who was carrying the Geminoid's head. Watching his bag go through the X-ray machine, I could clearly see the shape of a human head on the monitor. Everything inside was made of metal, which would be somewhat atypical for a real human, but the outline was clearly a head. I remember nervously watching the inspector's face, wondering if he would think that a murderer was trying to get by him.

The inspector of course asked my colleague to open his bag. As in Japan, I showed him a photograph of the Geminoid and explained that this was its head. Thankfully the inspector was familiar with our android. "I've seen this robot on television!" he said, clearly excited. He called a few others over to take a look, but in the end they let us through without a problem.

Since then I've had similar experiences when taking Geminoids to countries such as the United States and Australia. Security personnel in those countries, too, are often familiar with our invention, so a quick explanation is generally enough to avoid undue drama. I expect that passing though airport security will only become easier as Geminoid's fame continues to grow.

Giving lectures via Geminoid HI-4

Delivering lectures overseas has become much easier since we developed Geminoid HI-4. An overseas lecture can in some cases require a commitment up to two years in advance. Further, many people are typically involved, so once that commitment is made it cannot be easily changed. In a pinch it might be possible to deliver a presentation via Skype or other teleconferencing system, but that doesn't provide the sense of presence that audiences prefer, making for a disappointing presentation. I myself have had the experience of feeling let down to find that a lecture I was attending would be delivered by Skype.

As I have described, however, Geminoids are both products of my research and part of my identity. Their sense of presence on stage is also very close to that of a human. A Geminoid is thus a fine vehicle for delivering lectures.

During Geminoid presentations, I do not remotely operate the android, but rather play an audio recording while a computer controls it to duplicate my head motions. To achieve this, I deliver my presentation in an anechoic chamber, recording it with a microphone and a video camera. My team then analyzes the captured video to reproduce my head movements. We have recently improved the system so the android can automatically recognize faces in the audience and direct its gaze toward them.

In this way I am now able to automatically deliver lectures with no further effort from myself. Since I'm taping my lectures, I can re-record as necessary to make any needed corrections, making the final result far more polished than anything I could deliver live. When forced to speak in real-time, there's always the chance that I won't be feeling well or something will distract me, preventing me from speaking smoothly. Having my Geminoid autonomously deliver talks makes for a much more reliable presentation.

One current limitation, however, is that I have no way of automatically responding to questions. Audience questions are often difficult to hear, even when delivering a talk in person, and it will be a long time before voice recognition technologies are sufficiently advanced to overcome this problem. Even if speech could be automatically recognized, no sufficiently advanced technology for providing appropriate answers to audience questions has been developed. I must therefore be available to answer any questions via the Internet.

Interestingly, many audience members experience the illusion that the Geminoid itself is answering questions when in reality I'm responding via remote control. The main presentation and my responses to questions are both delivered in my voice, and it can be very difficult to distinguish between what was prerecorded and what is being spoken live. Apparently, many people don't notice any difference at all. The difference between the two modes can be further blurred by making small talk with the audience before the presentation, switching to automatic replay to deliver the talk, then going back to remote control to answer questions.

My Geminoid receives an invitation

A few months after I started delivering lectures via Geminoid, I received an invitation to an artificial intelligence conference in Spain. The letter, which was addressed "Dear Copy of Prof. Ishiguro," stated that since Dr. Ishiguro himself would likely be too busy to attend, the organizers wondered if my Geminoid would be kind enough to come in my place. Having no good reason to refuse, I sent a young researcher at my lab along with a Geminoid.

The presentation there was quite a success. After the talk ended, a line of people formed up in front of the android, hoping to ask questions or have their photograph taken with it. Indeed, this time spent interacting with the audience lasted longer than the presentation itself. This had never happened to me when giving a talk in person. Several times I've had people come up to introduce themselves or to ask for a photograph with me, but I've never had a line form. With the accompanying researcher's permission, many of those having their photographs taken put their arm around the android's shoulder or gave it a hug, smiling all the while. I was also surprised to find that around half of those posing for photos were women, in contrast to the stereotype of mainly men being AI students and researchers.

As I've described before, operating a Geminoid for a long time adapts you to it, so much so that when the android is touched you feel as if you have been touched. This can get awkward when one woman after another is pressing themselves against you to have their photograph taken. I wondered if they'd be doing the same thing if I was there in person. Would they still come drape an arm around me? No, of course not. This was only the case because I was using the body of a Geminoid.

Note that having a Geminoid deliver talks has benefits for event organizers as well. I, for one, would definitely prefer to invite a Geminoid rather than a real person to a conference I was hosting.

The first issue is cost. Inviting a guest speaker usually means purchasing a business-class airline ticket for them, and this can be very expensive for a guest coming from Europe. If a support technician comes instead, the host institution can supply a much less expensive economy-class ticket, and dissembling the Geminoid into three parts means its shipping costs will at most involve excess baggage fees for one bag.

Furthermore, when a Geminoid gives a talk related to robot technology, the audience can see the robot in action as well as listen to the talk. Should only a university professor arrive, they simply hear a presentation. Inviting a Geminoid therefore cuts costs in half and provides a demonstration of robot technology, delivering four times the value.

In previous chapters I discussed how creating Geminoids has given me opportunities to reflect on my own identity, but this situation showed me that my Geminoid contains part of that identity. Even after I leave this world, my Geminoid will remain, continuing to give lectures as before.

Sharing experiences with Geminoid

Now that I've given many Geminoid-mediated lectures both in Japan and overseas, people often tell me they've heard my talks, when actually it was a Geminoid they saw. This has made me realize that those attending the lectures do not distinguish between me and my Geminoid to the extent that I do. Of course, I suppose this is exactly what I should expect, since my Geminoid shares my identity.

My experiences exist not only as memories in my own head, but also in the memories of many others I interact with in society. This makes sense, since the limits of my own memory capacity prevent me from remembering everything about myself. The combined memory capacities of the countless people who surround me add up to a tremendous amount, however, making it possible to record far more memories than I ever could on my own.

Not only that, but our limited memories cause us to be selective in what we remember, with a bias toward remembering only what is convenient for us. In contrast, those around us remember both the good and the bad; more than once, I've had someone remind me of some unpleasant thing I've done in the past. Given that society views me and my Geminoid as being to some extent the same, it must also assume that the two of us share the same experiences.

Geminoid today can only recreate previously recorded lectures, but as development of autonomous functioning advances, it should become able to act according to its own judgment and entirely without my knowledge. Yet since our identities are elided over in the mind of the public, I may well be held responsible for its actions—even if someone with malicious intent reprograms the Geminoid or remotely controls it to perform some nefarious deed.

Geminoid behavior will become increasingly autonomous as technology advances. As that occurs, it will become increasingly important to consider security issues related to Geminoids that are copies of actual persons.

Androids as comedians

In 2012 I was involved in creating an android based on Katsura Beicho, a *rakugo* [traditional comic storytelling] artist designated by the Japanese government as a Living National Treasure. The experience taught me that I am not the only one who might be preserved for posterity through a shared identity with an android.

Mr. Katsura was already quite old and was in semi-retirement, so we were tasked with developing an android who could perform in his place for an event commemorating his eighty-eighth birthday. With the assistance of a modeling artist and a mechanical design engineer I'd worked with for many years, I believe we created an extremely high-quality product.

The biggest topic of discussion during this android's development was its apparent age. As of 2012, several years had passed since Mr. Katsura's last television appearance, meaning the general public was unfamiliar with how he now looked. Indeed, most people's image of him dated to when he was designated a Living National Treasure, which had boosted

his notoriety. We decided the public acknowledgement Mr. Katsura received at that time likely represented the peak of his identity, and therefore his android should represent that point in his life.

We did not create a cast as we had done for my androids and the others. Instead, we used a contactless three-dimensional scanner to measure the form of Mr. Katsura's head, then used

An android version of Katsura Beicho.

photographs from around 2000 to

recreate the appearance that most people were familiar with.

Mr. Katsura attended the media event we held to present his android after its completion. His immediate reaction to being presented with an android that looked just as he had a decade before was a joking "Oh, that's awful," suggesting that it was so similar to himself as to be creepy. He had of course cooperated in the process of making the android and wasn't opposed to the idea on principle, but apparently he found the actual experience of being presented with a duplicate of himself to be very strange.

After the android was displayed at Mr. Katsura's birthday event, his son and successor Yonedanji and I were invited to bring it to exhibitions and presentations at various museums and other venues. Typically, this involved a storytelling session by the Katsura android followed by more storytelling by Yonedanji, then a presentation by me. The audiences enjoyed the world of traditional comic storytelling, and I felt that the sessions had a broader appeal than typical *rakugo*; something about having an android relating the stories made them accessible not only to longtime fans of the art, but to younger people as well. In that sense, the android makes skillful use of Katsura's identity to continue showing people the appeal of his art, even in these years following his death.

I can imagine my android carrying on my identity in a similar way after my own death by giving lectures with a lifelike presence. In the sense that so long as our androids are maintained they can continue accumulating experience in society, we might even consider them a form of immortality for Mr. Katsura and myself.

MINIMAL HUMAN DESIGN: TELENOIDS

Creating a minimal human

Up to this point, I've talked about my attempts to make androids as humanlike as possible. As I wrote in the Prologue, however, this is not my true goal. Rather, while my interest in android research was sparked by my realization that a device's appearance is incredibly important, what I truly wish to do is identify the elements of humanity crucial to human–machine interactions. I've been researching androids for over ten years now, but I still do not have scientific answers to all of my questions. Even so, the past decade has provided me with a deep intuition as to where the answers may lie.

In the summer of 2009, I had the idea of bringing together only those elements essential to human interaction in a kind of minimal human form. While still pursuing the nature of humanity, this would take me in completely the opposite direction from my work with Geminoids. Namely, I would attempt to subtract rather than add elements of humanness while creating a robot that others would still recognize as humanlike.

When developing a new kind of robot, it is common practice to follow a straightforward and clear developmental policy. For example, in the case of Robovie, the first daily-life robot I created, I didn't consider design at all; my developmental policy was simply to use the most robust parts I could find so the robot would stably operate for as long as possible. For my Geminoids and other androids, my primary guideline was to create robots that looked highly humanlike. With this new endeavor, however, I wanted to bend the rules a bit. Now that my aim was to create a minimal humanlike form, I couldn't restrain myself to a single design policy. I would need to extract and compile varied ideas from among all my previous experiences.

Robovie and the Geminoids were not goals in and of themselves. Rather, they were means by which I could perform simple tests of my ideas. With this robot, however, I had found a kind of ultimate form that I wished to create. As soon as I had this idea, a very specific image came to mind. I named it "Telenoid."

Humanness without extraneous elements

It turned out to be harder than I expected to realize the image in my mind. After several attempts, I settled on Telenoid's final design just a week before the end of 2009.

I started with sketches. After that, I bought some clay and started making models. When sketching, it didn't take long to come up with something similar to what I was imagining. Transferring those sketches to three-dimensional form in clay, however, was far more difficult: no matter how hard I tried, I couldn't come up with a design that looked right from all angles. I therefore decided to hire a professional.

The first designer I hired was an acquaintance. I told him I was after a minimal human form, but all the sketches he produced contained extraneous elements. By "minimal" I meant the complete absence of any adornment or character. But apparently a request like that goes against the grain of a professional designer, especially one who has worked on robots before. Such designers have their own techniques for creating characteristics that tend to inform their designs. Telling such a person to eliminate any hint of character is akin to telling them to create a design-less design, which almost feels like a breach of etiquette. I tried a different designer, but the results were largely the same.

Giving up on professional designers, I went back to searching for ideas regarding how to put my mental image into three-dimensional form. Someone introduced me to a craftsperson who specializes in creating stuffed animals, and I gave them the clay model that looked most like what I was imagining, requesting a doll in that form. One advantage to this approach, I thought, would be that the soft materials used to

A model of how I imagined Telenoid, created in papier-mâché.

create stuffed animals might be a good way to represent human skin. Unfortunately, however, once again the result was not what I'd imagined. Stuffed animals have prominent seams and a limited range of forms, so it was difficult to use this medium to precisely realize my ideas.

In the end, I designed the Telenoid myself using a computerized modeling system, which allowed me to produce models thirty times faster than when working in clay. When modeling in clay, ensuring horizontal symmetry alone takes significant time, but on a computer this operation is nearly instantaneous, as are commands for producing overall roundness.

That being said, creating form from nothing is difficult, even when using a computer. This led me to think about an explicit design policy.

What I wanted to make was a robot that looked clearly human, but had no elements unnecessary for conversing with an actual human. In my final design, features disappear toward the bodily extremities, bringing your focus to the eyes, the most important element in dialogue. This design was humanlike, but provided no hints regarding specific age or gender.

With the aid of an assistant familiar with CAD software, the design only took around four hours to create. I gave simple instructions like "Make the head a little larger," or "Make these parts symmetric," and my assistant immediately reflected those changes in the computer model. When it was complete, a 3D printer converted it into tangible (acrylic) form overnight.

An image of Telenoid, created via computer graphics.

Using this acrylic model as a template, we next remade it using various materials. Doing so only required creating a mold and filling it with the desired material, an easy process. We first tried plaster, but of course that was too hard to produce a humanlike result. I discussed the problem with Yamato Nobuo, CEO of

Vstone Co., Ltd., a robotics startup I launched with some friends. This company had also created the Telenoid mold. Yamato suggested we use a material called Hitohada Gel, a resin that feels remarkably like human skin. Vstone was able to produce a prototype in about a week. As soon as I held it, I knew it was exactly what I'd been imagining.

The model was small enough to fit in one hand. Our next task was to reproduce the same form on a more human scale. Unlike the previous androids I'd created, I wanted this one to be highly portable and suited to broad dissemination. At this point, I started gathering a team to help me with the new project.

"I can't stop touching it"

I had built my previous androids with the help of Kokoro Company, Ltd. As I've described, those androids used pneumatic actuators in mechanisms that would operate stably for long periods, producing extremely humanlike movements with no unnatural sounds. Using pneumatic actuators for Telenoid, however, would have necessitated the use of a compressor for the air supply, making it impossible to carry around. A truly portable robot required mechanisms that operate using normal servomotors and batteries. Vstone is quite accomplished at creating such mechanisms, having previously developed many miniaturized humanoid robots. Even so, Vstone's technology was insufficient to build the robot I had in mind.

I wanted to cover the robot in a humanlike skin, so I asked Kokoro to handle its exterior appearance. Considering the varied applications we wanted Telenoid to serve, I also needed a partner to help with software development. For that, I teamed up with Eager Co., Ltd., a company I had worked with on robot theater. Eager is very skilled at developing software that allows robots to reproduce highly humanlike behaviors.

When inviting members to join a project team, one usually provides a clear description of exactly what is to be accomplished. However, that was difficult in this case. While admittedly a weak explanation, I started by simply telling everyone I wanted to create a minimal human form. I doubt they understood what I meant, but I was relieved to see they were willing to work together anyway.

I gathered everyone together and showed them the model we had come up with. "I want to recreate this as an eighty-centimeter robot," was the first thing I said. I still vividly remember everyone's reaction. Normally, one might expect them to ask, "Just what is this?" or "What does this thing do?" Or they might reply, "Let us take this back to our offices and think about it." But none expressed any doubts. Everyone nodded without hesitation and said, "Let's do it."

I suppose they figured they would let the details sort themselves out over time. Or maybe they just thought, *That Ishiguro is doing something strange again, but he seems serious. We might as well play along.* Whatever the case, everyone at the meeting was clearly enthralled with the curious design of this new robot, and our discussion became very lively.

This is how research differs from work toward practical applications— there's no need to justify every little decision. Indeed, most elements in an actual robot have no irrefutable basis for existing. We might provide some flimsy reason for why this part is shaped the way it is, or why that sensor was needed, but we can never say why it has to be exactly how we created it. Usually we do things because we've always done them that way, or because we got the idea from some other robot. The priority is to find something that seems interesting and give it a try. Everyone in our group felt that spark of interest, and I think that's ultimately why they agreed to work with us.

Upon reflection, I believe that following your intuition in this way to take on new challenges is more important in research than in product development. New possibilities arise when we take on such challenges. Current research in the fields of robotics and information media, however, seems far more conservative.

In any case, this is how research and development for Telenoid, the minimal humanoid android, began. Kokoro would make its skin, Vstone would manufacture its internal mechanisms, and Eager would work with ATR to create a remote operation system.

After development started, we produced a series of prototypes, each of which we discussed in a meeting while passing them around to touch. Some team members said they looked like babies, while others said they looked feminine. One said they looked like me. Once they held one, however, for some reason everyone said, "I can't stop touching it." Clearly, we were on our way to creating something with a unique appeal.

Why might people want to keep touching Telenoid? As mentioned above, it was designed so that its extremities appear to fade away when one looks at its eyes. Its eyes are very humanlike, but its arms and legs vanish at the edge of the visual field. It has a somewhat adult face, but one that is highly symmetrical, and its lack of eyebrows gives it an androgynous appearance. At the same time, the ratio of its face to its head size is that of a child's, making its age ambiguous as well. Its body retains some vestiges of thighs and buttocks, but it is fundamentally asexual. Its skin is a silicone covering that feels much like human skin.

In other words, as mentioned above, Telenoid looks and even feels very human, but has an undefined age and gender. It is unlike anything we normally encounter in day-to-day life. When we encounter an unknown figure of this sort, we typically endeavor to find out who or what it is. I think that when we see another human, we first try to identify them as an individual and then decide whether they are human, rather than immediately categorizing them as human or not. Put another way, we hold many examples of humans and animals in our heads. Therefore, before distinguishing between people and animals, we first recognize what or who is before our eyes, and only then obtain an abstract un-

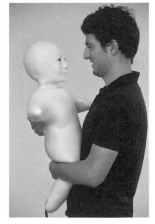

The highly touchable, 80-cm Telenoid.

derstanding of whether it is human or animal; we cannot jump directly to that abstract understanding.

Given that, even when confronted with the highly neutral appearance of a Telenoid, we go to great lengths to identify it. The biggest hints come from its voice. This enables us to project the face we imagine based on its voice onto the neutral canvas of its face. Other important clues are its texture and smell. Of similar importance to such objective information is the emotional state of those speaking with a Telenoid, which can cause it to look either angry or happy.

I believe the appeal of Telenoid derives precisely from its neutral appearance, which allows it to reflect the varied imaginings of its viewers. This is similar to the masks used in noh drama, which despite being fundamentally expressionless take on various appearances according to the music or scene. In the context of daily conversation, Telenoid, too, appears to have various expressions depending on the human's psychological state and the conditions under which it is being used, making it a remotely controlled android capable of taking on varied identities.

Children, couples, and the elderly

While the robotic system for Telenoid is highly simplified, it is in essence the same as that used in Geminoids. The system has three primary components: a main body, a separate computer with a camera for remote operation, and an external camera used to record the Telenoid and people conversing with it. The operator watches the Telenoid and anyone speaking with it via the computer, which displays images captured by the external camera. During these conversations, the computer camera captures the operator's expressions, analyzing lip and head movements and sending this data so that Telenoid can move in the same way. The operator's voice is simultaneously replayed from the android.

Telenoid's internal mechanisms are far simpler than those in Geminoid, which were designed to look as humanlike as possible. Since its appearance is also highly simplified, the android has a minimal number of moving parts: primarily its eyes, head, and arms, which together require eight motors. Unlike Geminoid, Telenoid's face is expressionless. This allows viewers to imagine its expression based on their psychological state and the voice they hear coming from it. This neutral expression stimulates the imagination of its human conversational partners. Readers who haven't experienced this may be skeptical, but I believe those who have interacted with a Telenoid will know what I mean.

When the first Telenoid prototype was complete, we tried using it with the general population in Austria and with elderly people in Japan. As I've described, in the autumn of 2009 we displayed Geminoid HI-1 at the Ars Electronica festival in Linz, Austria. In the following year, we took our just-completed Telenoid prototype to the same show.

Around half the people who came to our Telenoid exhibit said it looked eerie or creepy. Interestingly, however, their opinions changed as soon as they held it while it was being remotely controlled. Then, nearly everyone used words like "cute" and "fun" to describe it.

In particular, most young people visiting the exhibit when no one else was there kept their distance, saying Telenoid looked creepy. Nonetheless, they were curious and tended to stand there staring at it. When we handed it to them, suggesting they touch it, they immediately started having enjoyable conversations with it.

We also allowed attendees to operate the Telenoid while others conversed with it. Couples and child–adult pairs seemed to enjoy this experience most. When someone who appeared to be a schoolteacher operated Telenoid, a crowd of children gathered around it. We also saw the opposite age pattern: children operating the Telenoid and a group of somewhat elderly people competing to hold it.

The Telenoid display at the Ars Electronica festival.

These elders seemed to really enjoy their conversations, smiling as they peered at Telenoid's face and giving it hugs. Telenoid-mediated conversations between couples were more lively than usual, and several used the android for nearly thirty minutes. I was interested to see that as in the case of Geminoid, women seemed to be better operators than men.

Having experienced success in Austria, as soon as we returned to Japan we created an opportunity for elderly persons to use Telenoid. An elderly care center near the ATR laboratory brought forty or fifty residents for a tour, and we had them interact with the android while an elderly care center employee operated it.

Their reaction was quite different from what we expected. First, unlike the young people in Austria who called Telenoid "creepy" at first, none of these elderly people described its neutral expression as disturbing. They enjoyed conversing with Telenoid from the start, particularly while holding it. One even cried, saying it was like holding a real child.

Aside from its neutral expression, the biggest difference between Telenoid and Geminoid is that you can hold a Telenoid while you speak with it. (Although it might be possible to hug a Geminoid HI-1 or F during a conversation, few people would actually do so in public.) Holding something increases your familiarity with it, and when a voice comes from the Telenoid, it feels as if you are actually holding the person who is

"It's just like holding a real child."

speaking. This was true not only for elderly people, but also for those young people who considered Telenoid "creepy" until they held it themselves and changed their minds.

Almost no previous robots could be held like this. However, physical contact is an important part of sensing humanity. In fact, one feature of the Robovie robot I developed immediately after starting to study robots for human interaction was that it would say, "Hold me." Robovie did not have a soft body like Telenoid, but even so it was highly appealing to children, who loved to hug it.

Research and development related to human–machine conversation started with extremely simple interfaces like switches, followed by extensive research on speech-based dialogue functions. While this will aid these conversations, it is equally important for the robot to feel human-like when touched. We clearly have many ways of recognizing human-ness, and discovering how we can utilize physical contact with machines will be an important step toward achieving natural and stress-free interactions.

Robots as a substitute for mobile phones

With Geminoid F we achieved a significant cost reduction, but human lookalike androids were still far too expensive for purchase by the general public; both Geminoid F, which was designed to use the minimal mechanisms required for conversation, and Geminoid HI-4, which was even simpler, cost around 10,000,000 yen [around US$94,000]. This was far cheaper than Geminoid HI-1, which cost some 50–60,000,000 million yen, but still too high to tempt many people to purchase one for home use.

Of course, some very wealthy people might decide, for example, to skip buying a car and purchase a lookalike Geminoid instead, installing it at their faraway parents' home so they could talk whenever they wish. However, a Geminoid like that would generally be limited to their dedicated use. A Telenoid, in contrast, can help users recall the form of whomever they are speaking to, costs far less than a Geminoid, and can be used by anyone. I expect them to cost somewhere between 300,000 and 1,000,000 yen [around US$2,800 to $9,400].

Encouraged by this greatly reduced cost and the success of our preliminary experiments with elderly participants, we started working toward practical applications. Specifically, we aimed to develop Telenoids as a communication tool for the elderly.

The large number of elderly people living alone in Japan has become a societal problem. Mechanization has replaced much manual labor, so more jobs now require direct communication with others. More people are therefore traveling for work or taking distant posts, and many working households are moving to urban centers, leaving elderly parents behind. The number of elderly persons living alone will only increase in the future, and one of the most pressing issues they face is reduced opportunities for casual conversation with others. Such problems will be exacerbated as they become physically infirm, making it more difficult to leave home. This can eventually lead to illness. Using a remotely controlled robot to maintain communication should help alleviate many of the problems they face.

Monitoring the physical and psychological state of the elderly will of course become easier, but there will be many other benefits as well. Communication robots can alleviate problems related to use of email, telephones, and video calls, for instance. Some elderly persons have extreme difficulty using email by themselves. Indeed, anyone capable of using email will be able to take part in online social networks, allowing them to converse with a variety of people. Even telephones do not replicate the experience of talking with someone in person; they are merely a method for propagating information, and while they may seem easy to use, that is not the case for everyone. Video calls are potentially beneficial in that they allow speakers to see each other, but this can become a drawback when people feel they have to make themselves presentable before engaging in conversation. For this reason, I understand that while video conferencing is frequently used in business settings, its use for casual conversations is far more limited. Indeed, while most cell phones now have video call capabilities, many users, particularly the elderly, still prefer more traditional voice-only calls.

Compared with these forms of remote communication, Telenoid has many advantages. For one, it both acts as a telephone and allows us to feel the existence of the person we're speaking to. Even so, Telenoid operators need not worry about their current appearance, since they will not be shown to the person they are speaking with, as in the case of a video call. This will allow elderly persons to immediately initiate a conversation whenever needed, even late at night. The fact that Telenoids allow for physical contact is also important for the elderly. Light physical contact accompanying conversation both reinforces feelings of the other person's presence and provides a sense of security that cannot be obtained through speech alone.

In this way, Telenoid-based communications can help to prevent illness in the elderly. By frequently using a Telenoid to speak with various people, the elderly will get more exercise, and those speaking with them will more quickly take note of any changes in their health.

While extensive research will be needed to confirm this, I expect that use of a Telenoid will greatly reduce the number of illnesses and doctor visits among the elderly. Recent years have seen the development of various robots designed to aid the physical aspects of elder care, such as robotized beds that assist the elderly when getting up, or robots that help the elderly eat. Telenoids are designed for use before such care robots become necessary, providing communication support that may help delay their need.

A new kind of cell phone

I also invented a Telenoid-based cell phone, which I named "Elfoid." To allow for a broader range of applications, I developed Elfoid with the support of global telecommunications device supplier Qualcomm and Japanese mobile phone operator NTT Docomo.

In prototypes, we focused not on form, but on materials and communication functions. The Elfoid is shaped like a Telenoid, but only measures about twenty centimeters long. As with Telenoid, its exterior is coated in a covering that feels remarkably like human skin. Never before had a cell phone been created using such a soft material. Holding one almost feels like holding someone's hand.

Qualcomm provided us with a communications unit that only measured

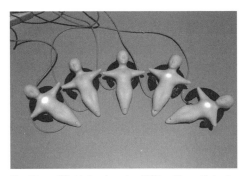

The 20-cm Elfoid, developed at ATR Intelligent Robotics and Communication Laboratories as a handheld cellular telephone.

around twenty millimeters on a side, but contained nearly all the functions of a modern cell phone. Some simple programming would thus make our prototype Elfoid a fully functioning cell phone, but we focused instead on functions supporting conversation. Simply put, we wanted Elfoid to support hands-free conversation. This was already a feature of most cell phones, but they generally could not play sounds very loudly. To improve this, we installed two large speakers in Elfoid's head so users could speak from a more natural distance.

This of course will not be Elfoid's final form. We will continue our research and development, incorporating sensors and actuators to make it more humanlike. But even with current prototypes, if usage conditions and users are controlled, it is possible to feel the presence of the person you are speaking with, right there in the palm of your hand. I suspect elderly people will especially appreciate being able to feel the presence of their children and grandchildren when speaking to them.

Smartphones have permeated society in recent years, but they do not represent an advancement in call functions. Yes, our phones now allow us to read email and browse the web, but telephone functions remain largely unchanged. So how might we further the advancement of call functions? One way would be to deliver a human presence to callers. In that sense, Elfoid may represent the next evolution in telephony.

Something we should keep in mind, however, is that every new technology brings the potential for nefarious uses. Put another way, any technology that would not be useful for criminals would not be useful to the general public. New and useful technologies are those with the power to change the world, and they will be used both for good and bad on their way to becoming an indispensable part of society. For example, research into nuclear forces led to the atomic bomb, but it also allowed us to generate electricity. The Internet has become an indispensable part of doing business, but it also exposes children to an inexhaustible supply of inappropriate content. I can't help but wonder how products like Telenoids and Elfoids might be misused if they are widely adopted. While I can only speculate, various possibilities come to mind.

One is a widespread scam called "It's me" in Japan, where fraudsters telephone elderly people pretending to be a relative to trick them out of money. Given that Elfoid provides a powerful sense of presence, it may make targets more likely to fall for this scam. We will need to seriously examine security issues related to Elfoid use.

True beauty comes from the imagination

Speaking of imagining beauty based on a voice, allow me to revisit the idea of what makes a person beautiful.

With Geminoid F, I wanted not only to create an android that looked exactly like its model, but one whose appearance, gestures, and speech mannerisms were attractive. What I found, however, was that trying to create a perfect human actually led away from humanness.

In contrast, while Telenoids look human, it isn't clear exactly who they look like. I did note, however, that when a man speaks to a Telenoid and it responds with an unknown but attractive female voice, he will imagine an idealized beauty. He almost feels as if he is holding that woman in his arms. Telenoids can thus generate virtual beauty.

I believe the beauty of Telenoids is actually greater than that of Geminoids. A Geminoid is a collection of a woman's most beautiful aspects, making it too beautiful to seem truly human. Even the most beautiful human has moments when they are not beautiful. A creature that is beautiful regardless of its facial expression or the situation in which it is viewed could only be a Geminoid-like android, and thus not quite human.

Of course, a beautiful person must first and foremost be human, so the beauty created in Geminoid is in principle an impossible beauty. The beauty in a Telenoid is better suited to human psychology. Imagine a person for whom you feel no attraction, until a certain moment when you suddenly start to find them extremely cute. If the appeal lingers, you might find yourself falling in love with that person and always feeling that same attraction. The visual information entering your brain has not changed, but you have discovered that person's attractiveness, affecting your visual perception to make that person look beautiful. This beauty born of imagination is the kind of beauty that Telenoids produce.

For me, research on androids and Geminoids was a study of the importance of appearance. Since starting to research Telenoids, however, I've learned that it is not necessarily important to exactly reproduce the appearance of a real human being. We humans use our imagination when viewing other humans. We do not rely exclusively on appearance when determining who we're looking at, what kind of person they are, and how attractive we find them. We view that person's expressions, listen to their voice, and make extensive use of our imagination before interpreting and understanding what kind of person they are.

Gestures, voices, and smells

Today, Telenoid's form remains incomplete. Since it will be applied to various situations, its functions will likely change in various ways. Even so, I don't believe its appearance will change much. Its design is the result of my own experiences and intuition, but so far I've had no reason to doubt its efficacy.

However, Telenoid's appearance makes other aspects, such as its voice and texture, very important for its humanness. These modalities become predominant, determining how the operator is perceived when communicating via the Telenoid.

As described above, the Telenoid's voice is very important. When emitting a female voice it appears female, and when speaking in a child's

CHAPTER 11 MINIMAL HUMAN DESIGN: TELENOIDS 159

voice it seems childlike. Using a voice changer to alter the operator's voice should therefore make Telenoid seem like a very different person. Even if the operator is male, artificially delivering his voice at a higher pitch makes users feel as if they are speaking with a woman.

After voice, sense of touch is highly important. The internal mechanisms in current Telenoids have a urethane covering, which is in turn covered by a silicone skin to produce a humanlike tactile experience. However, there is room to make them feel even more human. One way would be to use the previously-mentioned Hitohada Gel for skin. In future research, I would like to carefully select materials to test differences in users' response.

Smell follows sight and touch in importance. All humans have an odor, slight though it may be. Smell can be particularly useful in distinguishing men from women. The effective application of smell is an important topic for future research. Smell is the modality that most directly affects the brain, to the point where we cannot stand to be near offensive odors. What scents might provoke universal feelings of familiarity? The smell of a baby, perhaps, but that might make all Telenoids appear infantile. This might be fine when Telenoids are interacting with elderly people, but not in other situations.

Other elements are also no doubt important for creating a humanlike impression. An important part of future research will therefore be to determine exactly what human modalities are vital for an android to be accepted as humanlike, and to apply just those elements to produce a minimal human in the truest sense. By doing so, we might finally determine what is most important in the human–human and human–machine relationships I have investigated through my work with androids.

CHAPTER

12

A MINIMAL MEDIUM FOR SENSING PRESENCE: HUGVIE

The principle of minimal design

Since developing Telenoid, I have continued to pursue a truly minimal robot design that still created a sense of presence. A Telenoid has an ambiguous age and gender but retains minimal human features, which makes it a medium that any two people can use to interact based on their own power of imagination. Even so, I do not believe we can claim it has the absolute minimal design elements that still convey a feeling of human presence. What, then, would a truly minimal design look like?

I learned that in the case of Telenoid, users experienced the strongest sense of presence when they held it so as to hear the other person's voice right next to their ear. Everyone appeared to feel joy when hugging a Telenoid. This simple action created the illusion of holding the person they were talking to. Building on these insights, I developed a new minimal medium called "Hugvie" in 2012.

A Hugvie is simply a Telenoid-shaped huggable pillow with a pocket for holding a cell phone. Telenoids have an excellent form for reproducing the feeling of being hugged. Their arms are short enough to not get in the way, and their head and body are firm and easy to wrap one's arms around. I therefore searched for a material that would reproduce the feeling of embracing a human body while maintaining the Telenoid design. I settled on the microbeads that are often used in cushions and the like. We formed a stretchable fabric into the shape of a Telenoid, then filled it with enough microbeads to give it just the right firmness.

The Hugvie provides a strong sense of human presence.

While developing such an item may seem simple, in fact it took extensive effort. Using a stretchy material allowed us to reproduce the flexibility of a human body, but on the other hand made it difficult to retain Hugvie's form. Once that form is lost, it no longer feels as if you are hugging a human. We therefore had to produce prototype after prototype with varying fabric shapes and microbead amounts.

Once we had that sorted out, we added a pocket capable of holding a cell phone near where Hugvie's ear would be. To use the Hugvie, you simply put your cell phone into this pocket and talk to someone. It is a very simple medium. Even so, as I will describe in more detail below, it provides an extremely powerful sense of presence, far beyond what a cell phone alone can provide. Using a Hugvie truly feels as if you are talking to someone while holding them in your arms. But what about Hugvie allows it to so powerfully transmit this sense of presence?

When we successfully tie together two aspects, or modalities, of something, we feel a flash of recognition. This is an established tenet of philosophy. For example, when we see a form, we recall factors like its scent and warmth and then think, "Ah, I know what this is." Of course, recalling more factors, such as texture, intensifies this feeling of recognition, but that first moment when we link two aspects delivers the strongest jolt of recognition. If that's the case, we should be able to sense a human presence simply by being presented with two human modalities. Hugvie is a minimal medium that binds the two modalities of tactile sense ("huggability") and human voice, which is why it provides a strong sense of human presence.

This raises the question of what other modality pairs might similarly invoke a sense of presence. We tried removing the cell phone from Hugvie and applying perfume instead, providing the modalities of scent and tactile sense. Sure enough, this, too, provided a feeling of human presence. Holding this version of Hugvie was like hugging someone wearing perfume.

We next tried the combination of voice and scent. We placed a speaker behind test subjects and played voices from it. This alone was insufficient for providing a sense of presence, but as soon as we sprayed perfume they

---

reported feeling as if someone were standing behind them.

I will need to perform further research to confirm that two modalities are sufficient to invoke a sense of human presence, but I consider it a very credible hypothesis.

Hugvies relieve stress

I next performed a very interesting experiment to determine just how strong a sense of presence a Hugvie can provide. We had various people converse via Hugvie, and not only did all say they felt a strong sense of presence, they also reported being put at ease, or feeling as if they had developed a closer relationship. Several couples even said they grew closer after speaking by phone while both hugged a Hugvie.

This made me wonder whether Hugvie not only provided a sense of presence, but actually had a physical effect on subjects' bodies in the form of hormone release into the bloodstream. I decided to investigate this question using women aged forty to sixty as test subjects.

We compared subjects conversing via Hugvie with those using only a cell phone. We first tested subjects' blood and saliva to determine their level of cortisol, a hormone that rises above normal levels when we experience stress. We then had them converse with someone using either a Hugvie or a cell phone alone. We supplied the conversation partner and assigned a topic related to daily life. After an approximately fifteen-minute conversation, we retested their blood and saliva. The results showed a statistically significant decrease in cortisol levels in both blood and saliva with the Hugvie. All subjects also reported feeling relaxed while conversing via Hugvie.

These are important results, indicating that even a simple medium like Hugvie could be useful in medical applications such as stress reduction. Virtually no previous research on human–robot interactions has reported any effect on hormone levels. However, we were able to show that Hugvie puts its users at ease.

Children and Hugvie

Not only adults and the elderly, but children, too, enjoy using Hugvie. In an experiment where we read stories to children holding a Hugvie, we found that even normally excitable children were able to calm down and listen.

Small children want to constantly feel the presence of a parent. They also love dolls and stuffed animals, which they often want to keep nearby. A Hugvie may therefore be an excellent medium through which to provide a sense of presence.

As children age, they are freed from such insecurities, and by puberty have a strongly developed sense of self. At this point it is a boyfriend or girlfriend they want to feel the presence of, not a parent. Long-term desire for the presence of a partner eventually leads to marriage, bringing us back to a family and our own children. Those children repeat a similar pattern, spending their younger years desiring the presence of their parents, then passing through puberty and longing for the presence of another.

We thus spend our lives desiring the presence of others. One way to think of Hugvie, Telenoid, and even Geminoid is as robots developed to fulfill this basic human need.

How the brain recognizes humans

We developed androids and Geminoids to look like humans. These were followed by the minimal visual design of Telenoid, then by Hugvie, a minimal medium for providing a sense of presence during human interactions. If we think of these humanlike robots as lying on a coordinate axis, androids (or Geminoids) and Hugvies lay at opposite extremes.

The androids have a completely different appearance from Hugvie, but both robots are capable of interacting well with humans. So how do our brains perceive these two extreme examples of a humanoid robot? I would like to close this book with a discussion of the hypothesis that I currently consider most important in this respect. Namely, I believe there is a large difference in how the brain recognizes a highly humanlike android and how it recognizes a minimal robotlike Hugvie.

When perceiving a humanlike android, we compare sensory input related to individual modalities like appearance, motion, smell, and voice with the modality information stored in a mental model for recognizing other humans, and if the two match, we judge who among the people we know the android most resembles. In the case of someone who knows me, this mental model comprises a collection of memories regarding my features, such as my face, my expressions, my voice, and how I move.

When activating this model, an android must be humanlike in all its modalities. If the android's appearance or movements or any other aspect fail to be humanlike, our mental model detects this discrepancy and the android comes across as creepy. This is the so-called "uncanny valley" problem, and extreme care must be taken to avoid this when developing an android. Conversely, if all its modalities are humanlike, the android provides an extremely powerful sense of presence. Indeed, that presence will be so humanlike as to allow interactions in the real world.

In contrast, brain operations for recognizing Telenoid and Hugvie— Hugvie in particular—are very different. The age and gender of a Telenoid are indeterminate, but it looks human nonetheless. This neutral appearance does not come across as creepy. Rather, viewers use voice or other humanlike modalities to positively (and conveniently) interpret what they are seeing. This is similar to hearing an attractive male or female voice over the phone and imagining an equally attractive appearance without seeing the person there in front of you.

Further, our Hugvie research showed that two modalities are sufficient for recognition as a human, namely voice and tactile sense; voice reflects the speaker's individuality, while tactile sense provides a basis for feeling the speaker's presence. We reference a mental model for recognizing who we're speaking to, and that mental model helps us to imagine any missing modalities, such as appearance or movement. It is particularly interesting that we tend to imagine things positively, not in a negative way that would be inconvenient.

In both human–human and human–robot interactions, immediately obtaining all information about someone you've just met is not possible. We therefore use the extremely limited information we are able to obtain as a basis for imagining the rest. What if we were to imagine negative things about someone we'd just met, such as the bad things they might have done or the lies they might have told? We would never be able to speak with anyone we do not already know! Therefore, setting aside exceptions related to mental illness, we tend to select positive interpretations when we use our imagination to fill in the gaps about other people.

This is why people like Hugvies. They are given only two modalities, but that is sufficient to provide a sense of presence, and moreover allows them to always interact based on a positive image.

I will close with one more potential application for Hugvies. What if people used a Hugvie to speak with a coworker or an acquaintance with whom they were not very close? My guess is that the positive images complementing the Hugvie's voice and tactile sense might enable them to discover something good in that person.

Epilogue

Creating an android, especially one designed to be remotely controlled, provides both its developers and its operators with many discoveries and insights. In this book, I have related my own relevant experiences and those of people I've worked with, but what I have presented here is only a small fraction of what we've seen. More in-depth research based on the discoveries detailed in this book may provide new information allowing us to greatly expand our knowledge of human complexity. After we have compiled further research, I hope to once again pick up my pen and provide an update regarding what we have found.

I'd like to close this book by summarizing what I can confidently state regarding our findings so far. The most fundamental issues I address in my research are the definitions of self and humanity. These inquiries form the core of my research and are shared by many other people.

Regarding questions of self, all we have really discovered is that in some ways others know us better than we know ourselves, that we can only learn about ourselves through our experiences as members of society, and that others can act as mirrors for viewing ourselves. The question of who we are is a deep and fundamental one; a lifetime of research would likely not be enough to fully answer it. The experience of building an android, however, yields many leads to pursue. I hope that by reading this book you have gained some sense of the directions in which we might head.

I engaged in the research of humanlike androids because I wanted to better understand humanity and myself. I built them so that they could be controlled remotely control, and under specific conditions, one of these androids was able to take on my identity. In the context of limited interactions, then, androids can become nearly human.

However, there are limits on the extent to which androids can represent humans. Thanks to a very humanlike appearance and a highly emotional script, in android theater Geminoid F was able to represent a human so beautiful that even its model became jealous. Because that beauty transcended human beauty, however, it became something fundamentally different. It is interesting that we humans admire beings that exceed us, but this excess hinders our goal of understanding the essence of humanity.

I believe the beauty of androids stems from the fact that they do not make us think about the complex and multifaceted nature of humanity. Geminoid F is just too perfect a human. So how can we represent this complex and multifaceted nature? Should we create androids capable of more complex behaviors and expressions? That might be one approach. However, current technology constrains what we can depict, and creating an android as complex as a human will be no small feat.

After creating some extremely lifelike androids, therefore, I decided to go in the other direction and create robots with the minimal characteristics needed to represent a human being. Telenoid was the result.

The human complexity an android represents is an objective complexity. When looking at an android that is extremely similar to a particular human, we objectively sense a human being. In contrast, when looking at a Telenoid, a robot that evokes humanness but not a specific human, we sense its humanity subjectively. We must rely on our powers of imagination to project a specific person onto its neutral appearance.

I suspect that Telenoid, which appears to take on various facial expressions in various situations, will prove to be a more humanlike presence in the real world than will androids. We will likely have more luck representing human complexity through subjective rather than objective impressions. In other words, success is a question of how fully people can project onto androids a complexity based on their own experiences.

Recently, I have been actively involved in research and development of small humanoid robots that continue the concepts behind Telenoid.

These robots have very cute appearances, making them appealing to children. With these robots, I hope to capture children's ability to use their imagination when conversing with dolls. Like Telenoid they are cute and able to interact with people, but beyond that, they can interact as groups of multiple robots. Using these robots, I will engage in research and development related to how humans accept robots in the context of social interactions.

My biggest reason for wanting to develop small humanoid robots, however, is a desire to realize robots that will become more broadly incorporated into society. Unfortunately, building an android is expensive. In contrast, the fabrication costs for small humanoid robots have become low enough that they are appearing on the consumer market, and so present the possibility for widespread social adoption. Should that occur, these robots will allow deeper understanding of humans and human society. It is precisely this realization that will allow for a true exploration of humans through robots.

Of course, I also continue to research and develop androids and conventional robots. I believe continued explorations of such research will lead to understanding of topics that are extremely important and yet remain poorly understood, namely those related to human knowledge, consciousness, emotions, spirit, and soul. This understanding will come through emulating these human characteristics in androids and robots. Robots who are usable in society will teach us about human sociability, and furthermore provide us with a deep understanding of intelligence and other human-specific qualities. If we can realize robots who can interact with humans and become socially widespread, I believe a future filled with intellectual curiosity awaits us.

I wrote this book based on my research to date, but I have not been able to cover everything, and my work progresses every day. Readers who are interested in following my research can do so by visiting the website of my laboratory, the Department of System Creation at the Osaka University

Graduate School of Engineering (https://eng.irl.sys.es.osaka-u.ac.jp/), and that of ATR Hiroshi Ishiguro Laboratories (http://www.geminoid.jp/en/).

Ishiguro Hiroshi
September 2019

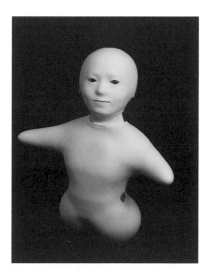

The redesigned Telenoid.

Acknowledgements

I could not have written this book without the support of the countless students and colleagues who aided me in my research, and the many others who supported me in various ways during that time. I express my sincerest thanks to them all.

About the Author

Ishiguro Hiroshi received a Ph.D. in systems engineering from Osaka University in 1991. He is currently a distinguished professor in the Department of Systems Innovation at Osaka University (2009–) and visiting director of Hiroshi Ishiguro Laboratories (2011–) at the Advanced Telecommunications Research Institute (ATR). He has published more than 300 papers for major journals and conferences. His robots have been highlighted more than 500 times in media including The Discovery Channel, NHK, and the BBC. In 2011, he won the Osaka Cultural Award, presented by the Osaka Prefectural Government and the Osaka City Government for his contributions to the advancement of culture in Osaka. In 2015, he received the Prize for Science and Technology (Research Category) from Japan's Minister of Education, Culture, Sports, Science and Technology.

About the Translator

Tony Gonzalez has been a translator of fiction, nonfiction, and technical works since 1988. Recent works of note include the *Math Girls* series (Bento Books), *The People and Culture of Japan*, and *Edo Japan Encounters the World* (Japan Publishing Industry Foundation for Culture). He lives in Atsugi, Japan.

（英文版）どうすれば「人」を創れるか：アンドロイドになった私
How Human Is Human?: The View from Robotics Research

2020 年 3 月 27 日　第 1 刷発行

著　者　　石黒　浩
訳　者　　トニー・ゴンザレス
発行所　　一般財団法人出版文化産業振興財団
　　　　　〒 101-0051 東京都千代田区神田神保町 2-2-30
　　　　　電話　03-5211-7283
　　　　　ホームページ　https://www.jpic.or.jp/

印刷・製本所　大日本印刷株式会社